The " Teaching of English " Series

General Editor—Dr. Richard Wilson

WORDSWORTH AND COLERIDGE

WILLIAM WORDSWORTH

No. 51

WILLIAM WORDSWORTH

WORDSWORTH AND COLERIDGE

Contrasted
by
GUY BOAS

February, August, October 1932; March, October 1935

THOMAS NELSON & SONS, LTD.
LONDON, EDINBURGH, AND NEW YORK

First Edition published May 1925
Reprinted December 1925; October 1929; January 1933:
February, August, October 1936; March, October 1938

CONTENTS

v

SAMUEL TAYLOR COLERIDGE

SAMUEL TAYLOR COLERIDGE

INTRODUCTION

To a generation which has passed through Arma-
geddon, the questions once so earnestly raised by the
publication of *Lyrical Ballads* may well seem to be
remote, and to need restating.

In the earlier half of the eighteenth century Alex-
ander Pope made high society the subject of his
poetry, and expressed himself in appropriately arti-
ficial language. Wordsworth, at the close of the same
century, declared a preference for " incidents and
situations from common life " and for " language
really used by men."

Certain critics, in expounding the ideals of the
Romantic Revival in English letters, seem to imply
that it was very wicked of Pope to use such exclusive
and " literary " language, and to confine himself in the
drawing-rooms of Queen Anne. How different from
Wordsworth, who walked among the people and took
a pride in sharing their speech : who was so truly
humble that he was prepared to learn wisdom from
children and shepherds, and delighted to commune
with a simple daisy. And so they turn Pope into a
naughty Sultan, and Wordsworth into a Saint Francis
of Assisi. To all of which, as Mr. Burchell said,
" Fudge."

Pope wrote *The Rape of the Lock*, which is a masterpiece ; Wordsworth wrote the *Ode on the Intimations
of Immortality*, which is another masterpiece ; and
the fact that these masterpieces have almost anti-
thetical qualities only proves the splendid variety of
English Literature.

The law of Art, as of Life, is change.   Action breeds
reaction, reaction spends itself, and

> " The world's great age begins anew,
>   The golden years return,
>   The earth doth like a snake renew
>   Her winter weeds outworn."

The pseudo-classical moulds into which Pope poured
his energy had served their purpose, and by 1798,
when *Lyrical Ballads* appeared, they were for the
time outworn.   So English poetry with the assistance
of Wordsworth and Coleridge changed its apparel in
order to begin anew.

The planning and composition of the *Ballads* have
been described so often, and so many just observations
have been made on the subject, that the commentary
has become almost as classic as the text.

Wordsworth's enthusiasm for the ideals of the
French Revolution had diminished in proportion as
the violence of that event increased.   A visit to Paris
in 1792, soon after the massacres of September, opened
his eyes to the potential meaning of Liberty and Fra-
ternity.   What enthusiasm he still retained for the
Republican cause suffered a further check : his rela-
tives effectively raised their voice in favour of the
ancient regime by stopping his allowance.   So he
returned abruptly to England, and to the pages of
Godwin, in which it was possible to study the theories
of Revolution without encountering the difficulties
of putting them into practice.   From *Political Justice*
Wordsworth learnt that perfect man is a being of pure
Intellect.   He exorcises all emotion and passion,
which are the misleading products of nefarious civil-
ization, and owns no authority, moral or otherwise,
except that of his own instinctive perception.

Wordsworth at heart was no iconoclast.   He was
attracted by Godwin, as by Rousseau, because at first
sight such teaching promises the Golden Age, which

is dear to the heart of every idealist. If the millennium could be won by theories, poets would be its natural heralds. But when experience shows that if Progress is too precipitate the result is blood and anarchy, poets are apt to return to the worship of Abstractions. The poetic instinct is not destructive, but creative, and to make a poem in praise of destruction is in a sense a paradox. The poetry of Shelley's *Queen Mab* is as positive as the *Code Napoleon :* its theories are as negative as the work of the guillotine.

Wordsworth was not content to make anarchy the subject of constructive art. If the Revolution did not lead to happiness, he must find it elsewhere, and looking out of his window upon the natural beauty of Dorset scenery, he saw the key to it. His lifework was to tell his fellow-men that if only they would look on Nature with seeing eyes, they too would learn the prescription for contentment.

The respectable guardians of the young poet were no more at ease over an enthusiasm for Nature than for the French Revolution. But, happily, a legacy of £900 from a young friend unexpectedly made Wordsworth his own modest master. With delight he persuaded his sister Dorothy to supervise his frugal house, and together, in 1797, they settled at Racedown in Dorset. At about the same time he met the other physician of his soul, the brilliant philosopher-poet-scientist - soldier - lecturer- journalist - social -reformer —Samuel Taylor Coleridge.

The early career of Coleridge had been as enthusiastic as Wordsworth's, and more varied. At the age of ten he astonished a schoolfellow, Charles Lamb, by the audacity of his thought. At Cambridge he conceived a passion for Liberty, upon which he discoursed by the hour from the depths of an armchair. Impatient of idle theory, he enlisted in the Light Dragoons ; impatient of strenuous practice, he returned to Cambridge : moved to Oxford, where, with Southey, he planned to found an ideal republic upon the banks of the Susquehanna ; and then to Bristol, where he wrote and lectured and conversed and issued a periodical, all with the intention of regenerating the world. During this period he first met Wordsworth, whom he found to be less a subject for conversion than for admiration.

The remarkable friendship which sprang up between the two great men caused Wordsworth to move to Alfoxden in Somerset, in order to be near Coleridge.

Lyrical Ballads

For men of poetic genius to attempt to collaborate is rare. A poet must be an egotist, otherwise his excuse for speaking where others are silent is gone. If poetry were the utterance of accumulated knowledge, or the expression of common sense, the art might be organized on a business footing, with clerks to write the manuscripts and a Board of Directors to furnish inspiration. But because the affair is individual, the poet must do his work alone, and though he may use his fellows as material or address them as an audience, he cannot combine with them as colleagues. Power comes into his heart from the hills, and not by way of his acquaintances.

Coleridge and Wordsworth did not long sustain their attempt to work together. But if they were imperfect colleagues, they were perfect friends. Each brought treasures of his own peculiarly acceptable to the other. To Wordsworth, lonely in his sense of potential and unappreciated power, Coleridge brought sympathy and admiration. " Wordsworth," wrote Coleridge, " is a very great man, the only man to whom *at all times and in all modes of excellence* I feel myself inferior." The fact that this was not true made the admiration all the more inspiring : what need of other testimony had a man to whom the author of *The Ancient Mariner* thus made obeisance ?

In return, to Coleridge's restless wandering spirit Wordsworth brought a short spell of stability and purpose. Instead of encouraging such futile and fantastic schemes as the Susquehanna Republic, Wordsworth kept the aspiration of his friend within a reasonable compass; the result was *The Ancient Mariner*, the greatest positive achievement in the life of Coleridge.

To the inspiration of mutual admiration was added that of a less spiritual type, thus recorded by Wordsworth :—

" In the spring of the year 1798, he [Coleridge], my sister, and myself, started from Alfoxden pretty late in the afternoon, with a view to visit Linton and the Valley of Stones near it ; and as our united funds were very small we agreed to defray the expense of the tour by writing a poem, to be sent to the *New Monthly Magazine*, set up by Philips, the bookseller, and edited by Dr. Aikin. Accordingly we set off, and proceeded along the Quantock Hills towards Watchet ; and in the course of this walk was planned the poem of *The Ancient Mariner*, founded on a dream, as Mr. Coleridge said, of his friend Mr. Cruikshanks. Much the greatest part of the story was Mr. Coleridge's invention ; but certain parts I myself suggested : for example, some crime was to be committed which should bring upon the Old Navigator, as Coleridge afterwards delighted to call him, the spectral persecution, as a consequence of that crime and his own wanderings. We began the composition together, on that, to me, memorable evening : I furnished two or three lines at the beginning of the poem. . . . As we endeavoured to proceed conjointly (I speak of the same evening), our respective manners proved so widely different, that it would have been quite presumptuous in me to do anything but separate from an undertaking upon which I could only have been a clog."

Scarcely have the poets conceived their first poem together than they must fall apart. Though Wordsworth speaks of presumption on his part, and of being a clog on his companion, he was in fact less humble than the words suggest. He does not say that his method is inferior, but that it is different, which is true, and will always be true where two poets of genius are concerned. Wordsworth, born in the rugged North country, remained always aloof and independent ; a power, sternly accepting life and the universe only upon his own terms, measured through his own vision, apprehended by his own " unconquerable mind." The sympathy which Coleridge, born in the soft South air of Devon, gave to Wordsworth he extended also to all the world. Where Wordsworth observes, Coleridge feels ; where Wordsworth judges, Coleridge explains. Wordsworth wished to saddle the Ancient Mariner with some crime so as to make the Albatross an example of moral retribution ; Coleridge would have been content to describe the bird, and leave it the unexplained phenomenon of a dream. In the pious conclusion of the poem, the influence of Wordsworth is apparent :

> " He prayeth best who loveth best
> All things both great and small :
> For the dear God, who loveth us,
> He made and loveth all."

The sentiment is appropriate when applied to Peter Bell's treatment of his donkey, but it is not in keeping with the spectral incidents of a narrative which should have preserved its quality of nightmare to the end.

The incongruous ending to the *Ancient Mariner* strikes at the heart of the difference between the two poets. Far reaches of the imagination into regions of the miraculous, the grotesque, and the inconsequent were natural to Coleridge ; the affairs of common day were the instinctive concern of Wordsworth.

How these inclinations were to determine what each was to contribute to *Lyrical Ballads*, Coleridge records in his *Biographia Literaria :*

" During the first year that Mr. Wordsworth and I were neighbours, our conversations turned frequently on the two cardinal points of poetry : the power of exciting the sympathy of the reader by a faithful adherence to the truth of nature, and the power of giving the interest of novelty by the modifying colours of imagination. . . . The thought suggested itself that a series of poems might be composed of two sorts. In the one, the incidents and agents were to be, in part at least, supernatural ; and the excellence aimed at was to consist in the interesting of the affections by the dramatic truth of such emotions as would naturally accompany such situations, supposing them real. . . . For the second class, subjects were to be chosen from ordinary life ; the characters and incidents were to be such as will be found in every village and its vicinity, where there is a meditative and feeling mind to seek after them, or to notice them, when they present themselves. In this idea originated the plan of *Lyrical Ballads ;* in which it was agreed that my endeavours should be directed to persons and characters supernatural. . . . Mr. Wordsworth, on the other hand, was . . . to give charm of novelty to things of every day."

Poems of Retribution

Though it does not occur among *Lyrical Ballads*, Peter Bell is the true counterpart of the Mariner. At the outset of each poem a wrong is committed, to be followed by prolonged retribution and by eventual repentance. But while the history of the Mariner is

marvellous, that of Wordsworth's potter is studiously
natural. The Mariner shoots an Albatross, the potter
beats his donkey : as an omen of wrath there appears
to the Mariner the skeleton ship upon the sky-line ;
the potter sees the corpse of the donkey's late master
in the river. The Mariner is terrified by the look from
his dead comrade's eyes, the potter is scared by leaves
that blow after him in the wind, by bloodstains caused
by the wounds which he had himself inflicted on the
ass, and by subterranean rumbling which proceeds
from miners at their daily task. The Mariner is won
back to repentance by all manner of supernatural
visions ; the potter by the prosaic voice of the
Methodist preacher. The compact made in *Lyrical
Ballads* is kept : Coleridge gives to romantic retribution " a semblance of truth " ; Wordsworth invests
commonplace retribution with an element " analogous
to the supernatural."

Poetic Diction

The verbal task which Wordsworth set himself in
Lyrical Ballads is elaborately explained in the Preface
to the second edition. As subjects for his poems,
" low and rustic life was generally chosen, because in
that condition the essential passions of the heart find
a better soil in which they can attain their maturity,
are less under restraint, and speak a plainer and more
emphatic language. . . . Such a language, arising out
of repeated experience and regular feelings, is a more
permanent, and a far more philosophical language,
than that which is frequently substituted for it by
Poets."

It is significant that the theories of the Preface were
only formulated after the composition of the first
volume. If the poet had them in mind to start with,
he did not adhere to them closely, and subsequently
he did not attend to them at all. At times he wrote

with signal success in accordance with his theory of Poetic Diction :

> " A violet by a mossy stone
>   Half hidden from the eye !
>   Fair as a star, when only one
>   Is shining in the sky."

Often he wrote in a style directly contrary to his theory, as when he describes the flight of the water-fowl :

> " Their jubilant activity evolves
>   Hundreds of curves and circlets, to and fro,
>   Upward and downward, progress intricate
>   Yet unperplexed, as if one spirit swayed
>   Their indefatigable flight."

Sometimes he follows a successful line obedient to his theory, with one disobedient, but as successful :

> " And while the young lambs bound
>   As to the tabor's sound . . . "

No great poet has ever been so fitfully inspired as Wordsworth, and no great poet has ever laboured so unremittingly when inspiration was absent. The banalities and absurdities which resulted have become classic :

The more Simon Lee works,

> " the more
> His poor old ankles swell."

Harry Gill

> " has a blanket on his back
> And coats enough to smother nine."

When the Idiot Boy does not return from his errand,

> " Betty is not quite at ease,
> And Susan has a dreadful night."

(2,604)

2

It is easy, but untrue, to lay the blame for such in-
eptitudes on the poet's loyalty to his verbal creed.
Lack of humour together with lack of inspiration is
their cause.   Wordsworth was certainly right in proclaiming that poetry is not the language of books, but
neither is it necessarily that of men : it is the language
of the gods.   And for the ankles of Simon Lee it is
the niggardly gods who are responsible.

Nature Poems

The conception of *Lyrical Ballads* was the only pre-
tence that the two poets could ever unite.   After the
publication of the first of the two volumes, each went
characteristically about his business, Wordsworth with
solemn industry, Coleridge fitfully, dejectedly, but
always brilliantly.

Coleridge continues to explore the sinister and marvellous in the unfinished *Christabel*, perpetuates the
evanescence of a dream in *Kubla Khan*, questions the
efficacy of Wordsworth's faith in *Dejection*, and writes
regretfully of love and hope and youth.   While thus
Coleridge sits piping with sympathetic mournfulness
to those who fall by the way, Wordsworth marches
steadily forward, a strong lonely prophet, anxious for
all to follow him, but impervious to individual needs.
He proclaims his profound gospel at the outset of
Lyrical Ballads :

> " One impulse from a vernal wood
>   May teach you more of man,
> Of moral evil and of good,
>   Than all the sages can."

From the blood of Paris and the stark intellect of
Godwin, the poet turns to Nature for a solution of
life.   Let man open his sensibilities to the beauty of

the sunset, the fragrance of flowers, the calm strength of mountains, the vitality of the vernal wood, and he will have understanding and peace.

The thought is in all that Wordsworth writes. At sight of the rainbow his heart " leaps up " with exaltation ; the daisy will " repair " it " with gladness " ; with the daffodils it " dances " ; the " meanest flower that blows " can give the poet " thoughts too deep for tears." This mystical conception of Nature is hard to understand, and harder to accept. A teacher of orthodox religion, when his transcendental appeal is not understood, may always take his stand upon simple ethics. It is not necessary fully to comprehend the Athanasian Creed in order to understand the Ten Commandments. The teaching of Wordsworth contains no simple moral code. The rainbow does not say " Thou shalt not steal," nor the daffodils " Thou shalt do no murder " : their influence is to have the same effect, but indirectly. Wordsworth insists that through contact with Nature the heart is exalted and made happy : such happiness and exaltation is moral, and in such a moral condition the heart can do no wrong.

It is easy to question the efficacy of this faith where the average man is concerned, but it is not possible to question Wordsworth's sincerity. One may argue that so to receive from Nature requires sensibilities which few possess ; but Wordsworth possessed them, and to doubt this is to doubt that he is not only a great poet but a great teacher.

To Coleridge Nature meant as much, but no more, than it does to any sensitive artist. He can describe a landscape as well as Wordsworth, and with a more subtle appreciation of contrast. But the scene signifies nothing more philosophical than beauty. He may for the moment, as in *Frost at Midnight*, express the Wordsworthian creed, but the expression springs from sympathy, not from conviction. At

another time he will put the contrary view, as in
Dejection :

> " O Lady ! we receive but what we give,
>   And in our life alone does nature live."

A prophet cannot afford to see both sides of his gospel;
and in the end simple uncompromising faith like that
of Saint Joan, of Cromwell, or of Wordsworth, carries
the greater weight.

Anamnesis

In the realm of philosophy, the mind of Wordsworth
was attracted to the Platonic theory of Anamnesis, or
recollection ; the idea that Paradise lies not in front
of, but behind the soul.

> " Our birth is but a sleep and a forgetting :
> The Soul that rises with us, our life's Star,
>   Hath had elsewhere its setting,
>   And cometh from afar :
>   Not in entire forgetfulness,
>   And not in utter nakedness,
> But trailing clouds of glory do we come
>   From God, who is our home.
> Heaven lies about us in our infancy !
> Shades of the prison-house begin to close
>   Upon the growing Boy,
> But he beholds the light, and whence it flows,
>   He sees it in his joy ;
> The Youth who daily further from the East
>   Must travel, still is Nature's priest,
>   And by the vision splendid
>   Is on his way attended ;
> At length the Man perceives it die away,
> And fade into the light of common day.

Anamnesis is a disheartening process, for which there
must be compensation. Such compensation Wordsworth found abundantly in the right contemplation

of Nature, the source of consolation and renewed
courage.

>   " . . . O ye Fountains, Meadows, Hills, and Groves,
>   Forebode not any severing of our loves !
>   Yet in my heart of hearts I feel your might ;
>   I only have relinquished one delight
>   To live beneath your more habitual sway."

To Coleridge the prison-house descends, and Nature
brings no redress ; the fountains and the meadows,
instead of fortifying themselves lose their glory, and
help to the aged does not even come from the hills.
Nature, indeed, becomes a tantalizing torment ; the
beauty of the clouds and the stars and the moon is
still visible, but is no longer potent.

>   " I see them all so excellently fair,
>   I see, not feel, how beautiful they are ! "

Bird Poems

Their difference of attitude to the life of Nature is
especially pointed when the poets address the birds of
the air.   To Coleridge a bird is enchanting, or a cause
of melancholy, but it is always a bird and nothing
more.   To Wordsworth bird-song is a perpetual sym-
bol of the Benevolence that rules the life of man.
The green linnet has a significance beside and beyond
its physical or vocal beauty.   It is a " life," a " presence " that purposely scatters its gladness among
men.   When the poet hears the skylark he feels contented with his fate, and is encouraged to plod on
with cheerfulness ; the bird has for him no empty
melody, but a song " of serious faith and inward
glee."   The cuckoo is

>   " no bird, but an invisible thing,
>   A voice, a mystery."

What a bird meant to Coleridge is extracted ruthlessly by the child's question :

" Do you ask what the birds say ? The sparrow, the dove,
    The linnet and thrush say, ' I love and I love.' "

The fact that without doubt this is precisely what the linnet and the thrush do say carries the interpretation as far as possible from the spirit of Wordsworth. When Coleridge sings *To the Nightingale*, it is merely to pay formal compliments ; to call it " most musical of birds," a " minstrel of the moon," and to affirm that it is only melancholy because melancholy people have thought it so. The bird is made not a significant subject, but the aimless object of human thought. In the narrative of *The Raven*, Coleridge's bird is credited with human emotions and plays a human part in the story ; but as a bird it has neither significance nor even qualities. Another poem entitled *A Nightingale* makes the matter still clearer. Here the nightingale's fame

" Should share in Nature's immortality,
    A venerable thing ! and so his song
    Should make all Nature lovelier, and itself
    Be loved like Nature ! "

The bird should survive as an entertainer : in Wordsworth he should survive as a prophet. Coleridge would have men love the bird's song as a treat ; Wordsworth would have them learn wisdom from it as a revelation.

Poems of Love.

It is in keeping with Wordsworth's austere and intellectual philosophy that he wrote no poems which in the ordinary sense are poems of love. He distrusts the profoundest and most overmastering of human passions, suspecting that such emotion will cloud his vision. Even the youthful admiration for Lucy is a matter for wonder rather than delight, and seems told almost with reluctance. The poet's passion is strange, and the story is only fit to be whispered into the ear of another lover. It is curious irony that Wordsworth, who so often puzzled his audience with his worship of Nature, should speak with hesitation on a subject universally understood. In the story of Ruth he dwells not upon the rapture of love, but upon the suffering of one of love's victims : in *Laodamia* the insistence again is not upon the sweets of love, but upon stern moderation and control :

> " for the Gods approve
> The depth, and not the tumult, of the soul ;
> A fervent, not ungovernable love."

Coleridge, taking by nature a less cold view, celebrated rather than resented love's sovereignty :

> " All thoughts, all passions, all delights,
>   Whatever stirs this mortal frame,
> All are but ministers of Love,
>   And feed his sacred flame."

Love brings little more joy into his song than into that of Wordsworth's, but for a different reason. Partly owing to temperament, but chiefly to his addiction to drugs, a morbid and melancholy regret for the past took premature possession of Coleridge's mind, and love, instead of being celebrated as the inspiration of the present or the hope of the future, is mourned over as a vanished emblem of youth :

> " O the joys, that came down shower-like,
>   Of Friendship, Love, and Liberty,
>   Ere I was old ! "

But the poet seems old, long before the years warrant. " Men are April when they woo, December when they wed," says Rosalind. Coleridge is December even as a wooer.

National Poems

In the poems written by the two poets upon national themes, the voice of Wordsworth is the more practical. Though his sympathy with revolutionary ideals was short-lived, it was real ; and always in speaking of Liberty, he spoke to some definite purpose. To Coleridge Liberty remained a theory, a subject as good as any other for speculation and discussion.

Wordsworth sympathizes with Toussaint L'Ouverture in his practical misfortunes, invokes the shade of Milton to stir England to practical endeavour, and charges the Men of Kent to practical resistance. Coleridge, with little hold on events, addresses his national thoughts, less as a warning than a lecture, to the abstract spirit of Liberty.

" O native Britain ! O my Mother Isle !
  How shouldst thou prove aught else but dear and holy
  To me, who from thy lakes and mountain-hills,
  Thy clouds, thy quiet dales, thy rocks and seas,
  Have drunk in all my intellectual life ? . . . "

So questions Coleridge, among his *Fears in Solitude*. While Wordsworth is urging the English to arms, Coleridge thus meditates in the abstract on his affections for his country, a matter which Wordsworth in the hour of peril takes for granted. Coleridge cannot think of England except as " Albion," or Switzerland except as " Helvetia." Though his heart is in England's danger, his head is in the clouds, and for all his experience of the Light Dragoons, it is hard to fancy him a very redoubtable defence. Wordsworth one pictures shouldering a rifle in the line, with Coleridge at headquarters speculating upon the nature of war.

Epitaphs

In conclusion, it is not inappropriate to set side by side at the close of this volume two epitaphs—one by Coleridge, frankly personal, one by Wordsworth, written for " A Poet," who could be no one more fittingly than himself.

The characteristic cry of Coleridge from the stone is humble, melancholy, and very human in its thirst for sympathy and love. " A Poet," on the other hand, although his looks are modest, is not really humble. He has experienced deep impulses, and he has truth to impart ; contentedly he has enjoyed what others understand, nor has he need for human prayers. Sky and earth, hill and valley, were his friends in life, and he wants no other friends in death.

If imagination follows the poets yet further, into the Elysian Fields, it shrinks from picturing too absolute a transformation, and finds them as distinct from one another as ever : Wordsworth still drawing industrious strength from the flowers and the grass, and speaking of them in tones now childish, now sublime; Coleridge still brilliantly talking, surrounded, even with eternity at his disposal, by unfinished poems and unpractised schemes.

WORDSWORTH AND COLERIDGE

POEMS OF NATURE BY WORDSWORTH

Lines written in Early Spring

I HEARD a thousand blended notes,
While in a grove I sate reclined,
In that sweet mood when pleasant thoughts
Bring sad thoughts to the mind.

To her fair works did Nature link
The human soul that through me ran ;
And much it grieved my heart to think
What man has made of man.

Through primrose tufts, in that green bower,
The periwinkle trailed its wreaths ;
And 'tis my faith that every flower
Enjoys the air it breathes.

The birds around me hopped and played,
Their thoughts I cannot measure :—
But the least motion which they made
It seemed a thrill of pleasure.

The budding twigs spread out their fan,
To catch the breezy air ;
And I must think, do all I can,
That there was pleasure there.

If this belief from heaven be sent,
If such be Nature's holy plan,
Have I not reason to lament
What man has made of man ?

The Thorn

" THERE is a Thorn—it looks so old,
In truth, you'd find it hard to say
How it could ever have been young,
It looks so old and grey.
Not higher than a two years' child
It stands erect, this aged Thorn ;
No leaves it has, no prickly points ;
It is a mass of knotted joints,
A wretched thing forlorn.
It stands erect, and like a stone
With lichens is it overgrown.

" Like rock or stone, it is o'ergrown,
With lichens to the very top,
And hung with heavy tufts of moss,
A melancholy crop :
Up from the earth these mosses creep,
And this poor Thorn they clasp it round
So close, you'd say that they are bent
With plain and manifest intent
To drag it to the ground ;
And all have joined in one endeavour
To bury this poor Thorn for ever.

" High on a mountain's highest ridge,
Where oft the stormy winter gale
Cuts like a scythe, while through the clouds
It sweeps from vale to vale ;
Not five yards from the mountain path,
This Thorn you on your left espy ;
And to the left, three yards beyond,
You see a little muddy pond
Of water—never dry
Though but of compass small, and bare
To thirsty suns and parching air.

" And, close beside this aged Thorn,
There is a fresh and lovely sight,
A beauteous heap, a hill of moss,
Just half a foot in height.
All lovely colours there you see,
All colours that were ever seen ;
And mossy network too is there,
As if by hand of lady fair
The work had woven been ;
And cups, the darlings of the eye,
So deep is their vermilion dye.

" Ah me ! what lovely tints are there
Of olive green and scarlet bright.
In spikes, in branches, and in stars,
Green, red, and pearly white !
This heap of earth o'ergrown with moss,
Which close beside the Thorn you see,
So fresh in all its beauteous dyes,
Is like an infant's grave in size,
As like as like can be ;
But never, never any where,
An infant's grave was half so fair.

" Now would you see this aged Thorn,
This pond, and beauteous hill of moss,

You must take care and choose your time
The mountain when to cross.
For oft there sits between the heap
So like an infant's grave in size,
And that same pond of which I spoke,
A Woman in a scarlet cloak,
And to herself she cries,
' Oh misery ! oh misery !
Oh woe is me ! oh misery ! '

" At all times of the day and night
This wretched Woman thither goes ;
And she is known to every star,
And every wind that blows ;
And there, beside the Thorn, she sits
When the blue daylight's in the skies,
And when the whirlwind's on the hill,
Or frosty air is keen and still,
And to herself she cries,
' Oh misery ! oh misery !
Oh woe is me ! oh misery ! ' "

" Now wherefore, thus, by day and night,
In rain, in tempest, and in snow,
Thus to the dreary mountain-top
Does this poor Woman go ?
And why sits she beside the Thorn
When the blue daylight's in the sky,
Or when the whirlwind's on the hill,
Or frosty air is keen and still,
And wherefore does she cry ?—
O wherefore ? wherefore ? tell me why
Does she repeat that doleful cry ? "

" I cannot tell ; I wish I could ;
For the true reason no one knows ;
But would you gladly view the spot,
The spot to which she goes ;

The hillock like an infant's grave,
The pond—and Thorn, so old and grey ;
Pass by her door—'tis seldom shut—
And, if you see her in her hut—
Then to the spot away !
I never heard of such as dare
Approach the spot when she is there."

" But wherefore to the mountain-top
Can this unhappy Woman go ?
Whatever star is in the skies,
Whatever wind may blow ? "
" Full twenty years are past and gone
Since she (her name is Martha Ray)
Gave with a maiden's true good-will
Her company to Stephen Hill ;
And she was blithe and gay,
While friends and kindred all approved
Of him whom tenderly she loved.

" And they had fixed the wedding day,
The morning that must wed them both ;
But Stephen to another Maid
Had sworn another oath ;
And, with this other Maid, to church
Unthinking Stephen went—
Poor Martha ! on that woeful day
A pang of pitiless dismay
Into her soul was sent ;
A fire was kindled in her breast,
Which might not burn itself to rest.

" They say, full six months after this,
While yet the summer leaves were green,
She to the mountain-top would go,
And there was often seen.
What could she seek ?—or wish to hide ?
Her state to any eye was plain ;

She was with child, and she was mad ;
Yet often was she sober sad
From her exceeding pain.
O guilty Father—would that death
Had saved him from that breach of faith !

" Sad case for such a brain to hold
Communion with a stirring child !
Sad case, as you may think, for one
Who had a brain so wild !
Last Christmas-eve we talked of this,
And grey-haired Wilfred of the glen
Held that the unborn infant wrought
About its mother's heart, and brought
Her senses back again :
And, when at last her time drew near,
Her looks were calm, her senses clear.

" More know I not, I wish I did,
And it should all be told to you ;
For what became of this poor child
No mortal ever knew ;
Nay—if a child to her was born
No earthly tongue could ever tell ;
And if 'twas born alive or dead,
Far less could this with proof be said ;
But some remember well,
That Martha Ray about this time
Would up the mountain often climb.

" And all that winter, when at night
The wind blew from the mountain-peak,
'Twas worth your while, though in the dark,
The churchyard path to seek :
For many a time and oft were heard
Cries coming from the mountain head :
Some plainly living voices were ;
And others, I've heard many swear,

Were voices of the dead :
I cannot think, whate'er they say,
They had to do with Martha Ray.

" But that she goes to this old Thorn,
The Thorn which I described to you,
And there sits in a scarlet cloak
I will be sworn is true.
For one day with my telescope,
To view the ocean wide and bright,
When to this country first I came,
Ere I had heard of Martha's name,
I climbed the mountain's height :—
A storm came on, and I could see
No object higher than my knee.

" 'Twas mist and rain, and storm and rain :
No screen, no fence could I discover ;
And then the wind ! in sooth, it was
A wind full ten times over.
I looked around, I thought I saw
A jutting crag,—and off I ran,
Head-foremost, through the driving rain,
The shelter of the crag to gain ;
And, as I am a man,
Instead of jutting crag, I found
A Woman seated on the ground.

" I did not speak—I saw her face ;
Her face !—it was enough for me ;
I turned about and heard her cry,
' Oh misery ! oh misery ! '
And there she sits, until the moon
Through half the clear blue sky will go ;
And, when the little breezes make
The waters of the pond to shake,
As all the country know,

3

She shudders, and you hear her cry,
' Oh misery ! oh misery ! ' ''

" But what's the Thorn ? and what's the pond ?
And what the hill of moss to her ?
And what the creeping breeze that comes
The little pond to stir ? ''
" I cannot tell ; but some will say
She hanged her baby on the tree ;
Some say she drowned it in the pond,
Which is a little step beyond :
But all and each agree,
The little Babe was buried there,
Beneath that hill of moss so fair.

" I've heard, the moss is spotted red
With drops of that poor infant's blood ;
But kill a new-born infant thus,
I do not think she could !
Some say, if to the pond you go,
And fix on it a steady view,
The shadow of a babe you trace,
A baby and a baby's face,
And that it looks at you ;
Whene'er you look on it, 'tis plain
The baby looks at you again.

" And some had sworn on oath that she
Should be to public justice brought ;
And for the little infant's bones
With spades they would have sought.
But instantly the hill of moss
Before their eyes began to stir !
And, for full fifty yards around,
The grass—it shook upon the ground !
Yet all do still aver
The little Babe lies buried there,
Beneath that hill of moss so fair.

" I cannot tell how this may be,
But plain it is the Thorn is bound
With heavy tufts of moss that strive
To drag it to the ground ;
And this I know, full many a time,
When she was on the mountain high,
By day, and in the silent night,
When all the stars shone clear and bright,
That I have heard her cry,
' Oh misery ! oh misery !
Oh woe is me ! oh misery ! ' "

Yarrow Unvisited *

FROM Stirling castle we had seen
The mazy Forth unravelled ;
Had trod the banks of Clyde, and Tay,
And with the Tweed had travelled ;
And when we came to Clovenford,
Then said my " *winsome Marrow*,"
" Whate'er betide, we'll turn aside,
And see the Braes of Yarrow."

" Let Yarrow folk, *frae* Selkirk town,
Who have been buying, selling,
Go back to Yarrow, 'tis their own ;
Each maiden to her dwelling !
On Yarrow's banks let herons feed,
Hares couch, and rabbits burrow !
But we will downward with the Tweed,
Nor turn aside to Yarrow.

" There's Galla Water, Leader Haughs,
Both lying right before us ;

* See the various poems the scene of which is laid upon the banks
of the Yarrow ; in particular, the exquisite Ballad of Hamilton
beginning

" Busk ye, busk ye, my bonny, bonny Bride,
Busk ye, busk ye, my winsome Marrow !—"

And Dryborough, where with chiming Tweed
The lintwhites sing in chorus ;
There's pleasant Tiviot-dale, a land
Made blithe with plough and harrow :
Why throw away a needful day
To go in search of Yarrow ?

" What's Yarrow but a river bare,
That glides the dark hills under ?
There are a thousand such elsewhere
As worthy of your wonder."
—Strange words they seemed of slight and scorn :
My True-love sighed for sorrow ;
And looked me in the face, to think
I thus could speak of Yarrow !

" Oh ! green," said I, " are Yarrow's holms,
And sweet is Yarrow flowing !
Fair hangs the apple frae the rock,
But we will leave it growing.
O'er hilly path, and open Strath,
We'll wander Scotland thorough ;
But, though so near, we will not turn
Into the dale of Yarrow.

" Let beeves and home-bred kine partake
The sweets of Burn-mill meadow ;
The swan on still St. Mary's Lake
Float double, swan and shadow !
We will not see them ; will not go,
To-day, nor yet to-morrow,
Enough if in our hearts we know
There's such a place as Yarrow.

" Be Yarrow stream unseen, unknown !
It must, or we shall rue it :
We have a vision of our own ;
Ah ! why should we undo it ?

The treasured dreams of times long past,
We'll keep them, winsome Marrow !
For when we're there, although 'tis fair,
'Twill be another Yarrow !

" If Care with freezing years should come,
And wandering seem but folly,—
Should we be loth to stir from home,
And yet be melancholy ;
Should life be dull, and spirits low,
'Twill soothe us in our sorrow,
That earth has something yet to show,
The bonny holms of Yarrow ! "

Yarrow Visited *

September 1814

AND is this—Yarrow ?—*This* the Stream
Of which my fancy cherished,
So faithfully, a waking dream ?
An image that hath perished !
O that some Minstrel's harp were near,
To utter notes of gladness,
And chase this silence from the air,
That fills my heart with sadness !

* As mentioned in my verses on the death of the Ettrick Shepherd,
my first visit to Yarrow was in his company. We had lodged the
night before at Traquhair, where Hogg had joined us, and also Dr.
Anderson, the Editor of the British Poets, who was on a visit at the
Manse. Dr. A. walked with us till we came in view of the Vale of
Yarrow, and, being advanced in life, he then turned back. The old
Man was passionately fond of poetry, though with not much of a
discriminating judgment, as the Volumes he edited sufficiently
show. But I was much pleased to meet with him, and to acknow-
ledge my obligation to his collection, which had been my brother
John's companion in more than one voyage to India, and which he
gave me before his departure from Grasmere, never to return.
Through these Volumes I became first familiar with Chaucer, and so
little money had I then to spare for books, that, in all probability,
but for this same work, I should have known little of Drayton,

Yet why ?—a silvery current flows
With uncontrolled meanderings :
Nor have these eyes by greener hills
Been soothed, in all my wanderings.
And, through her depths, Saint Mary's Lake
Is visibly delighted ;
For not a feature of those hills
Is in the mirror slighted.

A blue sky bends o'er Yarrow vale,
Save where that pearly whiteness
Is round the rising sun diffused,
A tender hazy brightness ;
Mild dawn of promise ! that excludes
All profitless dejection ;
Though not unwilling here to admit
A pensive recollection.

Where was it that the famous Flower
Of Yarrow Vale lay bleeding ?
His bed perchance was yon smooth mound
On which the herd is feeding :
And haply from this crystal pool,
Now peaceful as the morning,
The Water-wraith ascended thrice—
And gave his doleful warning.

Delicious is the Lay that sings
The haunts of happy Lovers,
The path that leads them to the grove,
The leafy grove that covers :

Daniel, and other distinguished poets of the Elizabethan age, and
their immediate successors, till a much later period of my life. I
am glad to record this, not from any importance of its own, but as
a tribute of gratitude to this simple-hearted old man, whom I never
again had the pleasure of meeting. I seldom read or think of this
poem without regretting that my dear Sister was not of the party, as
she would have had so much delight in recalling the time when,
travelling together in Scotland, we declined going in search of this
celebrated stream, not altogether, I will frankly confess, for the
reasons assigned in the poem on the occasion.

And Pity sanctifies the Verse
That paints, by strength of sorrow,
The unconquerable strength of love ;
Bear witness, rueful Yarrow !

But thou, that didst appear so fair
To fond imagination,
Dost rival in the light of day
Her delicate creation :
Meek loveliness is round thee spread,
A softness still and holy ;
The grace of forest charms decayed,
And pastoral melancholy.

That region left, the vale unfolds
Rich groves of lofty stature,
With Yarrow winding through the pomp
Of cultivated nature ;
And, rising from those lofty groves,
Behold a Ruin hoary !
The shattered front of Newark's Towers,
Renowned in Border story.

Fair scenes for childhood's opening bloom,
For sportive youth to stray in ;
For manhood to enjoy his strength ;
And age to wear away in !
Yon cottage seems a bower of bliss,
A covert for protection
Of tender thoughts, that nestle there—
The brood of chaste affection.

How sweet, on this autumnal day,
The wild-wood fruits to gather,
And on my True-love's forehead plant
A crest of blooming heather !
And what if I enwreathed my own !
'Twere no offence to reason ;

The sober Hills thus deck their brows
To meet the wintry season.

I see—but not by sight alone,
Loved Yarrow, have I won thee ;
A ray of fancy still survives—
Her sunshine plays upon thee !
Thy ever-youthful waters keep
A course of lively pleasure ;
And gladsome notes my lips can breathe,
Accordant to the measure.

The vapours linger round the Heights,
They melt, and soon must vanish ;
One hour is theirs, nor more is mine—
Sad thought, which I would banish,
But that I know, where'er I go,
Thy genuine image, Yarrow !
Will dwell with me—to heighten joy,
And cheer my mind in sorrow.

Yarrow Revisited

[The following stanzas are a memorial of a day passed with Sir Walter Scott and other Friends visiting the Banks of the Yarrow under his guidance, immediately before his departure from Abbotsford, for Naples.]

THE gallant Youth, who may have gained,
　　Or seeks, a " winsome Marrow,"
Was but an Infant in the lap
　　When first I looked on Yarrow ;
Once more, by Newark's Castle-gate
　　Long left without a warder,
I stood, looked, listened, and with Thee,
　　Great Minstrel of the Border !

Grave thoughts ruled wide on that sweet day,
　　Their dignity installing

In gentle bosoms, while sere leaves
　Were on the bough, or falling ;
But breezes played, and sunshine gleamed—
　The forest to embolden ;
Reddened the fiery hues, and shot
　Transparence through the golden.

For busy thoughts the Stream flowed on
　In foamy agitation ;
And slept in many a crystal pool
　For quiet contemplation :
No public and no private care
　The freeborn mind enthralling,
We made a day of happy hours,
　Our happy days recalling.

Brisk Youth appeared, the Morn of youth,
　With freaks of graceful folly,—
Life's temperate Noon, her sober Eve,
　Her Night not melancholy ;
Past, present, future, all appeared
　In harmony united,
Like guests that meet, and some from far,
　By cordial love invited.

And if, as Yarrow, through the woods
　And down the meadow ranging,
Did meet us with unaltered face,
　Though we were changed and changing ;
If, *then*, some natural shadows spread
　Our inward prospect over,
The soul's deep valley was not slow
　Its brightness to recover.

Eternal blessings on the Muse,
　And her divine employment !
The blameless Muse, who trains her Sons
　For hope and calm enjoyment ;

Albeit sickness, lingering yet,
  Has o'er their pillow brooded ;
And Care waylays their steps—a Sprite
  Not easily eluded.

For thee, O SCOTT ! compelled to change
  Green Eildon-hill and Cheviot
For warm Vesuvio's vine-clad slopes :
  And leave thy Tweed and Tiviot
For mild Sorento's breezy waves ;
  May classic Fancy, linking
With native Fancy her fresh aid,
  Preserve thy heart from sinking !

Oh ! while they minister to thee,
  Each vying with the other,
May Health return to mellow Age
  With Strength, her venturous brother ;
And Tiber, and each brook and rill
  Renowned in song and story,
With unimagined beauty shine,
  Nor lose one ray of glory !

For Thou, upon a hundred streams,
  By tales of love and sorrow,
Of faithful love, undaunted truth,
  Hast shed the power of Yarrow ;
And streams unknown, hills yet unseen,
  Wherever they invite Thee,
At parent Nature's grateful call,
  With gladness must requite Thee.

A gracious welcome shall be thine,
  Such looks of love and honour
As thy own Yarrow gave to me
  When first I gazed upon her ;
Beheld what I had feared to see,
  Unwilling to surrender

Dreams treasured up from early days,
  The holy and the tender.

And what, for this frail world, were all
  That mortals do or suffer,
Did no responsive harp, no pen,
  Memorial tribute offer ?
Yea, what were mighty Nature's self ?
  Her features, could they win us,
Unhelped by the poetic voice
  That hourly speaks within us ?

Nor deem that localized Romance
  Plays false with our affections ;
Unsanctifies our tears—made sport
  For fanciful dejections :
Ah, no ! the visions of the past
  Sustain the heart in feeling
Life as she is—our changeful Life,
  With friends and kindred dealing.

Bear witness, Ye, whose thoughts that day
  In Yarrow's groves were centred ;
Who through the silent portal arch
  Of mouldering Newark entered ;
And clomb the winding stair that once
  Too timidly was mounted
By the " last Minstrel," (not the last !)
  Ere he his Tale recounted.

Flow on for ever, Yarrow Stream !
  Fulfil thy pensive duty,
Well pleased that future Bards should chant
  For simple hearts thy beauty ;
To dream-light dear while yet unseen,
  Dear to the common sunshine,
And dearer still, as now I feel,
  To memory's shadowy moonshine !

Expostulation and Reply

" WHY, William, on that old grey stone,
Thus for the length of half a day,
Why, William, sit you thus alone,
And dream your time away ?

" Where are your books ?—that light bequeathed
To Beings else forlorn and blind !
Up ! up ! and drink the spirit breathed
From dead men to their kind.

" You look round on your Mother Earth,
As if she for no purpose bore you ;
As if you were her first-born birth,
And none had lived before you ! "

One morning thus, by Esthwaite lake,
When life was sweet, I knew not why,
To me my good friend Matthew spake,
And thus I made reply :

" The eye—it cannot choose but see ;
We cannot bid the ear be still ;
Our bodies feel, where'er they be,
Against or with our will.

" Nor less I deem that there are Powers
Which of themselves our minds impress ;
That we can feed this mind of ours
In a wise passiveness.

" Think you, 'mid all this mighty sum
Of things for ever speaking,
That nothing of itself will come,
But we must still be seeking ?

" —Then ask not wherefore, here, alone,
Conversing as I may,
I sit upon this old grey stone,
And dream my time away."

The Tables Turned

An Evening Scene on the same Subject

Up ! up ! my Friend, and quit your books ;
Or surely you'll grow double :
Up ! up ! my Friend, and clear your looks ;
Why all this toil and trouble ?

The sun, above the mountain's head,
A freshening lustre mellow
Through all the long green fields has spread,
His first sweet evening yellow.

Books ! 'tis a dull and endless strife :
Come, hear the woodland linnet,
How sweet his music ! on my life,
There's more of wisdom in it.

And hark ! how blithe the throstle sings !
He, too, is no mean preacher :
Come, forth into the light of things,
Let Nature be your teacher.

She has a world of ready wealth,
Our minds and hearts to bless—
Spontaneous wisdom breathed by health,
Truth breathed by cheerfulness.

One impulse from a vernal wood
May teach you more of man,
Of moral evil and of good,
Than all the sages can.

Sweet is the lore which Nature brings ;
Our meddling intellect
Mis-shapes the beauteous forms of things :—
We murder to dissect.

Enough of Science and of Art ;
Close up those barren leaves ;
Come forth, and bring with you a heart
That watches and receives.

Yew-Trees

THERE is a Yew-tree, pride of Lorton Vale,
Which to this day stands single, in the midst
Of its own darkness, as it stood of yore ;
Not loth to furnish weapons for the bands
Of Umfraville or Percy ere they marched
To Scotland's heaths ; or those that crossed the sea
And drew their sounding bows at Azincour,
Perhaps at earlier Crecy, or Poictiers.
Of vast circumference and gloom profound
This solitary Tree ! a living thing
Produced too slowly ever to decay ;
Of form and aspect too magnificent
To be destroyed.   But worthier still of note
Are those fraternal Four of Borrowdale,
Joined in one solemn and capacious grove ;
Huge trunks ! and each particular trunk a growth
Of intertwisted fibres serpentine
Up-coiling, and inveterately convolved ;
Nor uninformed with Phantasy, and looks
That threaten the profane ;—a pillared shade,
Upon whose grassless floor of red-brown hue,
By sheddings from the pining unbrage tinged
Perennially—beneath whose sable roof
Of boughs, as if for festal purpose, decked
With unrejoicing berries—ghostly Shapes

May meet at noontide ; Fear and trembling Hope,
Silence and Foresight ; Death the Skeleton
And Time the Shadow ;—there to celebrate,
As in a natural temple scattered o'er
With altars undisturbed of mossy stone,
United worship ; or in mute repose
To lie, and listen to the mountain flood
Murmuring from Glaramara's inmost caves.

Nutting

————————It seems a day
(I speak of one from many singled out)
One of those heavenly days that cannot die ;
When, in the eagerness of boyish hope,
I left our cottage-threshold, sallying forth
With a huge wallet o'er my shoulders slung,
A nutting-crook in hand ; and turned my steps
Tow'rd some far-distant wood, a Figure quaint,
Tricked out in proud disguise of cast-off weeds
Which for that service had been husbanded,
By exhortation of my frugal Dame—
Motley accoutrement, of power to smile
At thorns, and brakes, and brambles,—and, in truth,
More raggèd than need was ! O'er pathless rocks,
Through beds of matted fern, and tangled thickets,
Forcing my way, I came to one dear nook
Unvisited, where not a broken bough
Drooped with its withered leaves, ungracious sign
Of devastation ; but the hazels rose
Tall and erect, with tempting clusters hung,
A virgin scene !—A little while I stood,
Breathing with such suppression of the heart
As joy delights in ; and, with wise restraint
Voluptuous, fearless of a rival, eyed
The banquet ;—or beneath the trees I sate
Among the flowers, and with the flowers I played ;

A temper known to those, who, after long
And weary expectation, have been blest
With sudden happiness beyond all hope.
Perhaps it was a bower beneath whose leaves
The violets of five seasons re-appear
And fade, unseen by any human eye ;
Where fairy water-breaks do murmur on
For ever ; and I saw the sparkling foam,
And—with my cheek on one of those green stones
That, fleeced with moss, under the shady trees,
Lay round me, scattered like a flock of sheep—
I heard the murmur and the murmuring sound,
In that sweet mood when pleasure loves to pay
Tribute to ease ; and, of its joy secure,
The heart luxuriates with indifferent things,
Wasting its kindliness on stocks and stones,
And on the vacant air. Then up I rose,
And dragged to earth both branch and bough, with crash
And merciless ravage : and the shady nook
Of hazels, and the green and mossy bower,
Deformed and sullied, patiently gave up
Their quiet being : and, unless I now
Confound my present feelings with the past ;
Ere from the mutilated bower I turned
Exulting, rich beyond the wealth of kings,
I felt a sense of pain when I beheld
The silent trees, and saw the intruding sky—
Then, dearest Maiden, move along these shades
In gentleness of heart ; with gentle hand
Touch—for there is a spirit in the woods.

" I Wandered Lonely as a Cloud "

I WANDERED lonely as a cloud
That floats on high o'er vales and hills,
When all at once I saw a crowd,
A host, of golden daffodils ;

Beside the lake, beneath the trees,
Fluttering and dancing in the breeze.

Continuous as the stars that shine
And twinkle on the milky way,
They stretched in never-ending line
Along the margin of a bay :
Ten thousand saw I at a glance,
Tossing their heads in sprightly dance.

The waves beside them danced ; but they
Out-did the sparkling waves in glee :
A poet could not but be gay,
In such a jocund company :
I gazed—and gazed—but little thought
What wealth the show to me had brought :

For oft, when on my couch I lie
In vacant or in pensive mood,
They flash upon that inward eye
Which is the bliss of solitude ;
And then my heart with pleasure fills,
And dances with the daffodils.

Hart-leap Well

[Hart-leap Well is a small spring of water, about five miles from
Richmond in Yorkshire, and near the side of the road that leads from
Richmond to Askrigg.   Its name is derived from a remarkable Chase,
the memory of which is preserved by the monuments spoken of in the
second Part of the following Poem, which monuments do now exist
as I have there described them.]

THE Knight had ridden down from Wensley Moor
With the slow motion of a summer's cloud,
And now, as he approached a vassal's door,
" Bring forth another horse ! " he cried aloud.

" Another horse ! "—That shout the vassal heard
And saddled his best Steed, a comely grey ;

4

Sir Walter mounted him ; he was the third
Which he had mounted on that glorious day.

Joy sparkled in the prancing courser's eyes ;
The horse and horseman are a happy pair ;
But, though Sir Walter like a falcon flies,
There is a doleful silence in the air.

A rout this morning left Sir Walter's Hall,
That as they galloped made the echoes roar ;
But horse and man are vanished, one and all ;
Such race, I think, was never seen before.

Sir Walter, restless as a veering wind,
Calls to the few tired dogs that yet remain :
Blanch, Swift, and Music, noblest of their kind,
Follow, and up the weary mountain strain.

The Knight hallooed, he cheered and chid them on
With suppliant gestures and upbraidings stern ;
But breath and eyesight fail ; and, one by one,
The dogs are stretched among the mountain fern.

Where is the throng, the tumult of the race ?
The bugles that so joyfully were blown ?
—This chase it looks not like an earthly chase ;
Sir Walter and the Hart are left alone.

The poor Hart toils along the mountain-side ;
I will not stop to tell how far he fled,
Nor will I mention by what death he died ;
But now the Knight beholds him lying dead.

Dismounting, then, he leaned against a thorn ;
He had no follower, dog, nor man, nor boy :
He neither cracked his whip, nor blew his horn,
But gazed upon the spoil with silent joy.

Close to the thorn on which Sir Walter leaned,
Stood his dumb partner in this glorious feat ;
Weak as a lamb the hour that it is yeaned ;
And white with foam as if with cleaving sleet.

Upon his side the Hart was lying stretched :
His nostril touched a spring beneath a hill,
And with the last deep groan his breath had fetched
The waters of the spring were trembling still.

And now, too happy for repose or rest,
(Never had living man such joyful lot !)
Sir Walter walked all round, north, south, and west,
And gazed and gazed upon that darling spot.

And climbing up the hill—(it was at least
Four roods of sheer ascent) Sir Walter found
Three several hoof-marks which the hunted Beast
Had left imprinted on the grassy ground.

Sir Walter wiped his face, and cried, " Till now
Such sight was never seen by human eyes :
Three leaps have borne him from this lofty brow,
Down to the very fountain where he lies.

" I'll build a pleasure-house upon this spot,
And a small arbour, made for rural joy ;
'Twill be the traveller's shed, the pilgrim's cot,
A place of love for damsels that are coy.

" A cunning artist will I have to frame
A basin for that fountain in the dell !
And they who do make mention of the same,
From this day forth, shall call it HART-LEAP WELL.

" And, gallant Stag ! to make thy praises known,
Another monument shall here be raised ;
Three several pillars, each a rough-hewn stone,
And planted where thy hoofs the turf have grazed.

" And, in the summer-time when days are long,
I will come hither with my Paramour ;
And with the dancers and the minstrel's song
We will make merry in that pleasant bower.

" Till the foundations of the mountains fail
My mansion with its arbour shall endure ;—
The joy of them who till the fields of Swale,
And them who dwell among the woods of Ure ! "

Then home he went, and left the Hart, stone-dead,
With breathless nostrils stretched above the spring.
—Soon did the Knight perform what he had said ;
And far and wide the fame thereof did ring.

Ere thrice the Moon into her port had steered,
A cup of stone received the living well ;
Three pillars of rude stone Sir Walter reared,
And built a house of pleasure in the dell.

And near the fountain, flowers of stature tall
With trailing plants and trees were intertwined,—
Which soon composed a little sylvan hall,
A leafy shelter from the sun and wind.

And thither, when the summer days were long,
Sir Walter led his wondering Paramour ;
And with the dancers and the minstrel's song
Made merriment within that pleasant bower.

The Knight, Sir Walter, died in course of time,
And his bones lie in his paternal vale.—
But there is matter for a second rhyme,
And I to this would add another tale.

PART SECOND

The moving accident is not my trade ;
To freeze the blood I have no ready arts :
'Tis my delight, alone in summer shade,
To pipe a simple song for thinking hearts.

As I from Hawes to Richmond did repair,
It chanced that I saw standing in a dell
Three aspens at three corners of a square ;
And one, not four yards distant, near a well.

What this imported I could ill divine :
And, pulling now the rein my horse to stop,
I saw three pillars standing in a line,—
The last stone-pillar on a dark hill-top.

The trees were grey, with neither arms nor head ;
Half wasted the square mound of tawny green ;
So that you just might say, as then I said,
" Here in old time the hand of man hath been."

I looked upon the hill both far and near,
More doleful place did never eye survey ;
It seemed as if the spring-time came not here,
And Nature here were willing to decay.

I stood in various thoughts and fancies lost,
When one, who was in shepherd's garb attired,
Came up the hollow :—him did I accost,
And what this place might be I then inquired.

The Shepherd stopped, and that same story told
Which in my former rhyme I have rehearsed.
" A jolly place," said he, " in times of old !
But something ails it now : the spot is curst.

" You see these lifeless stumps of aspen wood—
Some say that they are beeches, others elms—

These were the bower ; and here a mansion stood,
The finest palace of a hundred realms !

" The arbour does its own condition tell ;
You see the stones, the fountain, and the stream ;
But as to the great Lodge ! you might as well
Hunt half a day for a forgotten dream.

" There's neither dog nor heifer, horse nor sheep,
Will wet his lips within that cup of stone ;
And oftentimes, when all are fast asleep,
This water doth send forth a dolorous groan.

" Some say that here a murder has been done,
And blood cries out for blood : but, for my part,
I've guessed, when I've been sitting in the sun,
That it was all for that unhappy Hart.

" What thoughts must through the creature's brain
     have past !
Even from the topmost stone, upon the steep,
Are but three bounds—and look, Sir, at this last—
O Master ! it has been a cruel leap.

" For thirteen hours he ran a desperate race ;
And in my simple mind we cannot tell
What cause the Hart might have to love this place,
And come and make his death-bed near the well.

" Here on the grass perhaps asleep he sank,
Lulled by the fountain in the summer-tide ;
This water was perhaps the first he drank
When he had wandered from his mother's side.

" In April here beneath the flowering thorn
He heard the birds their morning carols sing ;
And he, perhaps, for aught we know, was born
Not half a furlong from that self-same spring.

WILLIAM WORDSWORTH

"Now, here is neither grass nor pleasant shade;
The sun on drearier hollow never shone;
So will it be, as I have often said,
Till trees, and stones, and fountain, all are gone."

"Grey-headed Shepherd, thou hast spoken well;
Small difference lies between thy creed and mine:
This Beast not unobserved by Nature fell;
His death was mourned by sympathy divine.

"The Being, that is in the clouds and air,
That is in the green leaves among the groves,
Maintains a deep and reverential care
For the unoffending creatures whom he loves.

"The pleasure-house is dust:—behind, before,
This is no common waste, no common gloom;
But Nature, in due course of time, once more
Shall here put on her beauty and her bloom.

"She leaves these objects to a slow decay,
That what we are, and have been, may be known;
But at the coming of the milder day,
These monuments shall all be overgrown.

"One lesson, Shepherd, let us two divide,
Taught both by what she shows, and what conceals;
Never to blend our pleasure or our pride
With sorrow of the meanest thing that feels."

Composed upon Westminster Bridge

September 3, 1802

EARTH has not anything to show more fair:
Dull would he be of soul who could pass by
A sight so touching in its majesty:
This City now doth, like a garment, wear
The beauty of the morning; silent, bare,

Ships, towers, domes, theatres, and temples lie
Open unto the fields, and to the sky ;
All bright and glittering in the smokeless air.
Never did sun more beautifully steep
In his first splendour, valley, rock, or hill ;
Ne'er saw I, never felt, a calm so deep !
The river glideth at his own sweet will :
Dear God ! the very houses seem asleep ;
And all that mighty heart is lying still !

Vernal Ode

[Rerum Natura tota est nusquam magis quam in minimis.—PLIN.
Nat. Hist.]

BENEATH the concave of an April sky,
When all the fields with freshest green were dight,
Appeared, in presence of the spiritual eye
That aids or supersedes our grosser sight,
The form and rich habiliments of One
Whose countenance bore resemblance to the sun,
When it reveals, in evening majesty,
Features half lost amid their own pure light.
Poised like a weary cloud, in middle air
He hung,—then floated with angelic ease
(Softening that bright effulgence by degrees)
Till he had reached a summit sharp and bare,
Where oft the venturous heifer drinks the noontide
        breeze.
Upon the apex of that lofty cone
Alighted, there the Stranger stood alone ;
Fair as a gorgeous Fabric of the east
Suddenly raised by some enchanter's power,
Where nothing was ; and firm as some old Tower
Of Britain's realm, whose leafy crest
Waves high, embellished by a gleaming shower !

Beneath the shadow of his purple wings
Rested a golden harp ;—he touched the strings ;

And, after prelude of unearthly sound
Poured through the echoing hills around,
He sang—
         " No wintry desolations,
Scorching blight or noxious dew,
Affect my native habitations ;
Buried in glory, far beyond the scope
Of man's inquiring gaze, but to his hope
Imaged, though faintly, in the hue
Profound of night's ethereal blue ;
And in the aspect of each radiant orb ;—
Some fixed, some wandering with no timid curb :
But wandering star and fixed, to mortal eye—
Blended in absolute serenity,
And free from semblance of decline ;—
Fresh as if Evening brought their natal hour,
Her darkness splendour gave, her silence power
To testify of Love and Grace divine.

" What if those bright fires
Shine subject to decay,
Sons haply of extinguished sires,
Themselves to lose their light, or pass away
Like clouds before the wind,
Be thanks poured out to Him whose hand bestows,
Nightly, on human kind
That vision of endurance and repose.
—And though to every draught of vital breath
Renewed throughout the bounds of earth or ocean,
The melancholy gates of Death
Respond with sympathetic motion ;
Though all that feeds on nether air,
Howe'er magnificent or fair,
Grows but to perish, and entrust
Its ruins to their kindred dust ;
Yet, by the Almighty's ever-during care,
Her procreant vigils Nature keeps
Amid the unfathomable deeps ;

And saves the peopled fields of earth
From dread of emptiness or dearth.
Thus, in their stations, lifting tow'rd the sky
The foliaged head in cloud-like majesty,
The shadow-casting race of trees survive :
Thus, in the train of Spring, arrive
Sweet flowers ;—what living eye hath viewed
Their myriads ?—endlessly renewed,
Wherever strikes the sun's glad ray ;
Where'er the subtle waters stray ;
Wherever sportive breezes bend
Their course, or genial showers descend !
Mortals, rejoice ! the very Angels quit
Their mansions unsusceptible of change,
Amid your pleasant bowers to sit,
And through your sweet vicissitudes to range ! "

Oh, nursed at happy distance from the cares
Of a too-anxious world, mild pastoral Muse !
That, to the sparkling crown Urania wears,
And to her sister Clio's laurel wreath,
Prefer'st a garland culled from purple heath,
Or blooming thicket moist with morning dews ;
Was such bright Spectacle vouchsafed to me ?
And was it granted to the simple ear
Of thy contented Votary
Such melody to hear !
Him rather suits it, side by side with thee—
Wrapped in a fit of pleasing indolence,
While thy tired lute hangs on the hawthorn-tree,
To lie and listen—till o'er-drowsèd sense
Sinks, hardly conscious of the influence—
To the soft murmur of the vagrant Bee.
—A slender sound ! yet hoary Time
Doth to the *Soul* exalt it with the chime
Of all his years ;—a company
Of ages coming, ages gone ;
(Nations from before them sweeping,

Regions in destruction steeping,)
But every awful note in unison
With that faint utterance, which tells
Of treasure sucked from buds and bells,
For the pure keeping of those waxen cells :
Where She—a statist prudent to confer
Upon the common weal ; a warrior bold,
Radiant all over with unburnished gold,
And armed with living spear for mortal fight :
     A cunning forager
That spreads no waste ; a social builder ; one
In whom all busy offices unite
With all fine functions that afford delight—
Safe through the winter storm in quiet dwells !

And is She brought within the power
Of vision ?—o'er this tempting flower
Hovering until the petals stay
Her flight, and take its voice away !—
Observe each wing !—a tiny van !
The structure of her laden thigh,
How fragile ! yet of ancestry
Mysteriously remote and high ;
High as the imperial front of man ;
The roseate bloom on woman's cheek ;
The soaring eagle's curvèd beak ;
The white plumes of the floating swan ;
Old as the tiger's paw, the lion's mane
Ere shaken by that mood of stern disdain
At which the desert trembles.—Humming Bee !
Thy sting was needless then, perchance unknown,
The seeds of malice were not sown ;
All creatures met in peace, from fierceness free,
And no pride blended with their dignity.
—Tears had not broken from their source ;
Nor Anguish strayed from her Tartarean den ;
The golden years maintained a course
Not undiversified though smooth and even ;

We were not mocked with glimpse and shadow then,
Bright Seraphs mixed familiarly with men ;
And earth and stars composed a universal heaven !

Lines

*Composed a few miles above Tintern Abbey, on
revisiting the banks of the Wye during a Tour*

FIVE years have past ; five summers, with the length
Of five long winters ! and again I hear
These waters, rolling from their mountain-springs
With a soft inland murmur.*—Once again
Do I behold these steep and lofty cliffs,
That on a wild secluded scene impress
Thoughts of more deep seclusion ; and connect
The landscape with the quiet of the sky.
The day is come when I again repose
Here, under this dark sycamore, and view
These plots of cottage-ground, these orchard-tufts,
Which at this season, with their unripe fruits,
Are clad in one green hue, and lose themselves
'Mid groves and copses.   Once again I see
These hedge-rows, hardly hedge-rows, little lines
Of sportive wood run wild : these pastoral farms,
Green to the very door ; and wreaths of smoke
Sent up, in silence, from among the trees !
With some uncertain notice, as might seem
Of vagrant dwellers in the houseless woods,
Or of some Hermit's cave, where by his fire
The Hermit sits alone.
                        These beauteous forms,
Through a long absence, have not been to me
As is a landscape to a blind man's eye :
But oft, in lonely rooms, and 'mid the din
Of towns and cities, I have owed to them
In hours of weariness, sensations sweet,

* The river is not affected by the tides a few miles above Tintern.

Felt in the blood, and felt along the heart ;
And passing even into my purer mind,
With tranquil restoration :—feelings too
Of unremembered pleasure : such, perhaps,
As have no slight or trivial influence
On that best portion of a good man's life,
His little, nameless, unremembered acts
Of kindness and of love. Nor less, I trust,
To them I may have owed another gift,
Of aspect more sublime ; that blessed mood,
In which the burthen of the mystery,
In which the heavy and the weary weight
Of all this unintelligible world,
Is lightened :—that serene and blessed mood,
In which the affections gently lead us on,—
Until, the breath of this corporeal frame
And even the motion of our human blood
Almost suspended, we are laid asleep
In body, and become a living soul :
While with an eye made quiet by the power
Of harmony, and the deep power of joy,
We see into the life of things.

                                        If this
Be but a vain belief, yet, oh ! how oft—
In darkness and amid the many shapes
Of joyless daylight ; when the fretful stir
Unprofitable, and the fever of the world,
Have hung upon the beatings of my heart—
How oft, in spirit, have I turned to thee,
O sylvan Wye ! thou wanderer thro' the woods,
How often has my spirit turned to thee !
    And now, with gleams of half-extinguished thought,
With many recognitions dim and faint,
And somewhat of a sad perplexity,
The picture of the mind revives again :
While here I stand, not only with the sense
Of present pleasure, but with pleasing thoughts
That in this moment there is life and food

For future years. And so I dare to hope,
Though changed, no doubt, from what I was when first
I came among these hills ; when like a roe
I bounded o'er the mountains, by the sides
Of the deep rivers, and the lonely streams,
Wherever nature led : more like a man
Flying from something that he dreads, than one
Who sought the thing he loved. For nature then
(The coarser pleasures of my boyish days,
And their glad animal movements all gone by)
To me was all in all—I cannot paint
What then I was. The sounding cataract
Haunted me like a passion : the tall rock,
The mountain, and the deep and gloomy wood,
Their colours and their forms, were then to me
An appetite ; a feeling and a love,
That had no need of a remoter charm,
By thought supplied, nor any interest
Unborrowed from the eye.—That time is past,
And all its aching joys are now no more,
And all its dizzy raptures. Not for this
Faint I, nor mourn nor murmur ; other gifts
Have followed ; for such loss, I would believe,
Abundant recompense. For I have learned
To look on nature, not as in the hour
Of thoughtless youth ; but hearing oftentimes
The still, sad music of humanity,
Nor harsh nor grating, though of ample power
To chasten and subdue. And I have felt
A presence that disturbs me with the joy
Of elevated thoughts ; a sense sublime
Of something far more deeply interfused,
Whose dwelling is the light of setting suns,
And the round ocean and the living air,
And the blue sky, and in the mind of man ;
A motion and a spirit, that impels
All thinking things, all objects of all thought,
And rolls through all things. Therefore am I still

A lover of the meadows and the woods,
And mountains ; and of all that we behold
From this green earth ; of all the mighty world
Of eye, and ear,—both what they half create,
And what perceive ; well pleased to recognize
In nature and the language of the sense,
The anchor of my purest thoughts, the nurse,
The guide, the guardian of my heart, and soul
Of all my moral being.

                Nor perchance,
If I were not thus taught, should I the more
Suffer my genial spirits to decay :
For thou art with me here upon the banks
Of this fair river ; thou my dearest Friend,
My dear, dear Friend ; and in thy voice I catch
The language of my former heart, and read
My former pleasures in the shooting lights
Of thy wild eyes.   Oh ! yet a little while
May I behold in thee what I was once,
My dear, dear Sister ! and this prayer I make,
Knowing that Nature never did betray
The heart that loved her ; 'tis her privilege,
Through all the years of this our life, to lead
From joy to joy : for she can so inform
The mind that is within us, so impress
With quietness and beauty, and so feed
With lofty thoughts, that neither evil tongues,
Rash judgments, nor the sneers of selfish men,
Nor greetings where no kindness is, nor all
The dreary intercourse of daily life,
Shall e'er prevail against us, or disturb
Our cheerful faith, that all which we behold
Is full of blessings.   Therefore let the moon
Shine on thee in thy solitary walk ;
And let the misty mountain-winds be free
To blow against thee : and, in after years,
When these wild ecstasies shall be matured
Into a sober pleasure ; when thy mind

Shall be a mansion for all lovely forms,
Thy memory be as a dwelling-place
For all sweet sounds and harmonies ; oh ! then,
If solitude, or fear, or pain, or grief,
Should be thy portion, with what healing thoughts
Of tender joy wilt thou remember me,
And these my exhortations ! Nor, perchance—
If I should be where I no more can hear
Thy voice, nor catch from thy wild eyes these gleams
Of past existence—wilt thou then forget
That on the banks of this delightful stream
We stood together ; and that I, so long
A worshipper of Nature, hither came
Unwearied in that service : rather say
With warmer love—oh ! with far deeper zeal
Of holier love. Nor wilt thou then forget,
That after many wanderings, many years
Of absence, these steep woods and lofty cliffs,
And this green pastoral landscape, were to me
More dear, both for themselves and for thy sake !

The Healing Power of Nature,
from " The Prelude "

FROM Nature doth emotion come, and moods
Of calmness equally are Nature's gifts :
This is her glory ; these two attributes
Are sister horns that constitute her strength.
Hence Genius, born to thrive by interchange
Of peace and excitation, finds in her
His best and purest friend ; from her receives
That energy by which he seeks the truth,
From her that happy stillness of the mind
Which fits him to receive it when unsought.

Such benefit the humblest intellects
Partake of, each in their degree ; 'tis mine

To speak, what I myself have known and felt ,
Smooth task ! for words find easy way, inspired
By gratitude, and confidence in truth.
Long time in search of knowledge did I range
The field of human life, in heart and mind
Benighted ; but, the dawn beginning now
To reappear, 'twas proved that not in vain
I had been taught to reverence a Power
That is the visible quality and shape
And image of right reason ; that matures
Her processes by stedfast laws ; gives birth
To no impatient or fallacious hopes,
No heat of passion or excessive zeal,
No vain conceits ; provokes to no quick turns
Of self-applauding intellect ; but trains
To meekness, and exalts by humble faith ;
Holds up before the mind intoxicate
With present objects, and the busy dance
Of things that pass away, a temperate show
Of objects that endure ; and by this course
Disposes her, when over-fondly set
On throwing off incumbrances, to seek
In man, and in the frame of social life,
Whate'er there is desirable and good
Of kindred permanence, unchanged in form
And function, or, through strict vicissitude
Of life and death, revolving.   Above all
Were re-established now those watchful thoughts
Which, seeing little worthy or sublime
In what the Historian's pen so much delights
To blazon—power and energy detached
From moral purpose—early tutored me
To look with feelings of fraternal love
Upon the unassuming things that hold
A silent station in this beauteous world.

Thus moderated, thus composed, I found
Once more in Man an object of delight,
(2,604)

5

Of pure imagination, and of love ;
And, as the horizon of my mind enlarged,
Again I took the intellectual eye
For my instructor, studious more to see
Great truths, than touch and handle little ones.
Knowledge was given accordingly ; my trust
Became more firm in feelings that had stood
The test of such a trial ; clearer far
My sense of excellence—of right and wrong :
The promise of the present time retired
Into its true proportion ; sanguine schemes,
Ambitious projects, pleased me less ; I sought
For present good in life's familiar face,
And built thereon my hopes of good to come.

The Visit to the Cottage of The Solitary, from " The Excursion "

                              In genial mood,
While at our pastoral banquet thus we sate
Fronting the window of that little cell,
I could not, ever and anon, forbear
To glance an upward look on two huge Peaks
That from some other vale peered into this.
" Those lusty twins," exclaimed our host, " if here
It were your lot to dwell, would soon become
Your prized companions.—Many are the notes
Which, in his tuneful course, the wind draws forth
From rocks, woods, caverns, heaths, and dashing
        shores ;
And well those lofty brethren bear their part
In the wild concert—chiefly when the storm
Rides high ; then all the upper air they fill
With roaring sound, that ceases not to flow,
Like smoke, along the level of the blast,
In mighty current ; theirs, too, is the song
Of stream and headlong flood that seldom fails ;

And, in the grim and breathless hour of noon,
Methinks that I have heard them echo back
The thunder's greeting. Nor have nature's laws
Left them ungifted with a power to yield
Music of finer tone ; a harmony,
So do I call it, though it be the hand
Of silence, though there be no voice ;—the clouds,
The mist, the shadows, light of golden suns,
Motions of moonlight, all come thither—touch,
And have an answer—thither come, and shape
A language not unwelcome to sick hearts
And idle spirits :—there the sun himself,
At the calm close of summer's longest day,
Rests his substantial orb ;—between those heights
And on the top of either pinnacle,
More keenly than elsewhere in night's blue vault,
Sparkle the stars, as of their station proud.
Thoughts are not busier in the mind of man
Than the mute agents stirring there :—alone
Here do I sit and watch——"

                     A fall of voice,
Regretted like the nightingale's last note,
Had scarcely closed this high-wrought strain of rapture
Ere with inviting smile the Wanderer said :
" Now for the tale with which you threatened us ! "
" In truth the threat escaped me unawares :
Should the tale tire you, let this challenge stand
For my excuse.   Dissevered from mankind,
As to your eyes and thoughts we must have seemed
When ye looked down upon us from the crag,
Islanders 'mid a stormy mountain sea,
We are not so ;—perpetually we touch
Upon the vulgar ordinances of the world ;
And he, whom this our cottage hath to-day
Relinquished, lived dependent for his bread
Upon the laws of public charity.
The Housewife, tempted by such slender gains

As might from that occasion be distilled,
Opened, as she before had done for me,
Her doors to admit this homeless Pensioner ;
The portion gave of coarse but wholesome fare
Which appetite required—a blind dull nook,
Such as she had, the *kennel* of his rest !
This, in itself not ill, would yet have been
Ill borne in earlier life ; but his was now
The still contentedness of seventy years.
Calm did he sit under the wide-spread tree
Of his old age ; and yet less calm and meek,
Winningly meek or venerably calm,
Than slow and torpid ; paying in this wise
A penalty, if penalty it were,
For spendthrift feats, excesses of his prime.
I loved the old Man, for I pitied him !
A task it was, I own, to hold discourse
With one so slow in gathering up his thoughts,
But he was a cheap pleasure to my eyes ;
Mild, inoffensive, ready in *his* way,
And helpful to his utmost power ; and there
Our housewife knew full well what she possessed !
He was her vassal of all labour, tilled
Her garden, from the pasture fetched her kine ;
And, one among the orderly array
Of hay-makers, beneath the burning sun
Maintained his place ; or heedfully pursued
His course, on errands bound, to other vales,
Leading sometimes an inexperienced child
Too young for any profitable task.
So moved he like a shadow that performed
Substantial service.   Mark me now, and learn
For what reward !—The moon her monthly round
Hath not completed since our dame, the queen
Of this one cottage and this lonely dale,
Into my little sanctuary rushed—
Voice to a rueful treble humanized,
And features in deplorable dismay.

I treat the matter lightly, but, alas !
It is most serious ; persevering rain
Had fallen in torrents ; all the mountain tops
Were hidden, and black vapours coursed their sides
This had I seen, and saw ; but, till she spake,
Was wholly ignorant that my ancient Friend—
Who at her bidding, early and alone,
Had clomb aloft to delve the moorland turf
For winter fuel—to his noontide meal
Returned not, and now, haply, on the heights
Lay at the mercy of this raging storm.
' Inhuman ! '—said I, ' was an old Man's life
Not worth the trouble of a thought ?—alas !
This notice comes too late.'   With joy I saw
Her husband enter—from a distant vale.
We sallied forth together ; found the tools
Which the neglected veteran had dropped,
But through all quarters looked for him in vain.
We shouted—but no answer !   Darkness fell
Without remission of the blast or shower,
And fears for our own safety drove us home.

I, who weep little, did, I will confess,
The moment I was seated here alone,
Honour my little cell with some few tears
Which anger and resentment could not dry.
All night the storm endured ; and, soon as help
Had been collected from the neighbouring vale,
With morning we renewed our quest : the wind
Was fallen, the rain abated, but the hills
Lay shrouded in impenetrable mist ;
And long and hopelessly we sought in vain :
Till, chancing on that lofty ridge to pass
A heap of ruin—almost without walls
And wholly without roof (the bleached remains
Of a small chapel, where, in ancient time,
The peasants of these lonely valleys used
To meet for worship on that central height)—

We there espied the object of our search,
Lying full three parts buried among tufts
Of heath-plant, under and above him strewn,
To baffle, as he might, the watery storm :
And there we found him breathing peaceably,
Snug as a child that hides itself in sport
'Mid a green hay-cock in a sunny field.
We spake—he made reply, but would not stir
At our entreaty ; less from want of power
Than apprehension and bewildering thoughts.

So was he lifted gently from the ground,
And with their freight homeward the shepherds moved
Through the dull mist, I following—when a step,
A single step, that freed me from the skirts
Of the blind vapour, opened to my view
Glory beyond all glory ever seen
By waking sense or by the dreaming soul !
The appearance, instantaneously disclosed,
Was of a mighty city—boldly say
A wilderness of building, sinking far
And self-withdrawn into a boundless depth,
Far sinking into splendour—without end !
Fabric it seemed of diamond and of gold,
With alabaster domes, and silver spires,
And blazing terrace upon terrace, high
Uplifted ; here, serene pavilions bright,
In avenues disposed ; there, towers begirt
With battlements that on their restless fronts
Bore stars—illumination of all gems !
By earthly nature had the effect been wrought
Upon the dark materials of the storm
Now pacified ; on them, and on the coves
And mountain-steeps and summits, whereunto
The vapours had receded, taking there
Their station under a cerulean sky.
Oh, 'twas an unimaginable sight !
Clouds, mists, streams, watery rocks and emerald turf,

Clouds of all tincture, rocks and sapphire sky,
Confused, commingled, mutually inflamed,
Molten together, and composing thus,
Each lost in each, that marvellous array
Of temple, palace, citadel, and huge
Fantastic pomp of structure without name,
In fleecy folds voluminous, enwrapped.
Right in the midst, where interspace appeared
Of open court, an object like a throne
Under a shining canopy of state
Stood fixed ; and fixed resemblances were seen
To implements of ordinary use,
But vast in size, in substance glorified ;
Such as by Hebrew Prophets were beheld
In vision—forms uncouth of mightiest power
For admiration and mysterious awe.
This little Vale, a dwelling-place of Man,
Lay low beneath my feet ; 'twas visible—
I saw not, but I felt that it was there.
That which I *saw* was the revealed abode
Of Spirits in beatitude : my heart
Swelled in my breast—' I have been dead,' I cried,
' And now I live ! Oh ! wherefore *do* I live ? '
And with that pang I prayed to be no more !—
—But I forget our Charge, as utterly
I then forgot him :—there I stood and gazed :
The apparition faded not away,
And I descended.

            Having reached the house,
I found its rescued inmate safely lodged,
And in serene possession of himself,
Beside a fire whose genial warmth seemed met
By a faint shining from the heart, a gleam
Of comfort, spread over his pallid face.
Great show of joy the housewife made, and truly
Was glad to find her conscience set at ease ;
And not less glad, for sake of her good name,
That the poor Sufferer had escaped with life.

But, though he seemed at first to have received
No harm, and uncomplaining as before
Went through his usual tasks, a silent change
Soon showed itself : he lingered three short weeks ;
And from the cottage hath been borne to-day.

So ends my dolorous tale, and glad I am
That it is ended." At these words he turned—
And, with blithe air of open fellowship,
Brought from the cupboard wine and stouter cheer,
Like one who would be merry. Seeing this,
My grey-haired Friend said courteously—" Nay, nay,
You have regaled us as a hermit ought ;
Now let us forth into the sun ! "—Our Host
Rose, though reluctantly, and forth we went.

POEMS OF NATURE BY COLERIDGE

Hymn

Before Sun-rise, in the Vale of Chamouni

[Besides the rivers, Arve and Arveiron, which have their sources
in the foot of Mont Blanc, five conspicuous torrents rush down its
sides ; and within a few paces of the Glaciers, the *Gentiana Major*
grows in immense numbers with its " flowers of loveliest blue."]

HAST thou a charm to stay the morning-star
In his steep course ? So long he seems to pause
On thy bald awful head, O sovran Blanc !
The Arve and Arveiron at thy base
Rave ceaselessly ; but thou, most awful Form !
Risest from forth thy silent sea of pines,
How silently ! Around thee and above
Deep is the air and dark, substantial, black,
An ebon mass : methinks thou piercest it,
As with a wedge ! But when I look again,
It is thine own calm home, thy crystal shrine,
Thy habitation from eternity !
O dread and silent Mount ! I gazed upon thee,
Till thou, still present to the bodily sense,
Didst vanish from my thought : entranced in prayer
I worshipped the Invisible alone.

Yet, like some sweet beguiling melody,
So sweet, we know not we are listening to it,
Thou, the meanwhile, wast blending with my thought,

Yea, with my life and life's own secret joy :
Till the dilating Soul, enrapt, transfused,
Into the mighty vision passing—there
As in her natural form, swelled vast to Heaven !

Awake, my soul ! not only passive praise
Thou owest ! not alone these swelling tears,
Mute thanks and secret ecstasy ! Awake,
Voice of sweet song ! Awake, my Heart, awake !
Green vales and icy cliffs, all join my Hymn.

Thou first and chief, sole sovran of the Vale !
O struggling with the darkness all the night,
And visited all night by troops of stars,
Or when they climb the sky or when they sink :
Companion of the morning-star at dawn,
Thyself Earth's rosy star, and of the dawn
Co-herald : wake, O wake, and utter praise !
Who sank thy sunless pillars deep in Earth ?
Who filled thy countenance with rosy light ?
Who made thee parent of perpetual streams ?

And you, ye five wild torrents fiercely glad !
Who called you forth from night and utter death,
From dark and icy caverns called you forth,
Down those precipitous, black, jagged Rocks,
For ever shattered and the same for ever ?
Who gave you your invulnerable life,
Your strength, your speed, your fury, and your joy,
Unceasing thunder and eternal foam ?
And who commanded (and the silence came),
Here let the billows stiffen, and have rest ?

Ye ice-falls ! ye that from the mountain's brow
Adown enormous ravines slope amain—
Torrents, methinks, that heard a mighty voice,
And stopped at once amid their maddest plunge !
Motionless torrents ! silent cataracts !

Who made you glorious as the gates of Heaven
Beneath the keen full moon ?   Who bade the sun
Clothe you with rainbows ?   Who, with living flowers
Of loveliest blue, spread garlands at your feet ?—
God ! let the torrents, like a shout of nations,
Answer ! and let the ice-plains echo, God !
God ! sing ye meadow-streams with gladsome voice !
Ye pine-groves, with your soft and soul-like sounds !
And they too have a voice, yon piles of snow,
And in their perilous fall shall thunder, God !

Ye living flowers that skirt the eternal frost !
Ye wild goats sporting round the eagle's nest !
Ye eagles, play-mates of the mountain-storm !
Ye lightnings, the dread arrows of the clouds !
Ye signs and wonders of the element !
Utter forth God, and fill the hills with praise !

Thou too, hoar Mount ! with thy sky-pointing
    peaks,
Oft from whose feet the avalanche, unheard,
Shoots downward, glittering through the pure serene
Into the depth of clouds, that veil thy breast—
Thou too again, stupendous Mountain ! thou
That as I raise my head, awhile bowed low
In adoration, upward from thy base
Slow travelling with dim eyes suffused with tears,
Solemnly seemest, like a vapoury cloud,
To rise before me—Rise, O ever rise,
Rise like a cloud of incense, from the Earth !
Thou kingly Spirit throned among the hills,
Thou dread ambassador from Earth to Heaven,
Great hierarch ! tell thou the silent sky,
And tell the stars, and tell yon rising sun,
Earth, with her thousand voices, praises God.

This Lime-Tree Bower My Prison

[In the June of 1797, some long-expected Friends paid a visit to the Author's cottage ; and on the morning of their arrival he met with an accident, which disabled him from walking during the whole time of their stay. One evening, when they had left him for a few hours, he composed the following lines in the garden-bower.]

WELL, they are gone, and here must I remain,
This lime-tree bower my prison ! I have lost
Beauties and feelings, such as would have been
Most sweet to my remembrance even when age
Had dimmed mine eyes to blindness! They, meanwhile,
Friends, whom I never more may meet again,
On springy heath, along the hill-top edge,
Wander in gladness, and wind down, perchance,
To that still roaring dell, of which I told ;
The roaring dell, o'erwooded, narrow, deep,
And only speckled by the mid-day sun ;
Where its slim trunk the ash from rock to rock
Flings arching like a bridge ;—that branchless ash,
Unsunned and damp, whose few poor yellow leaves
Ne'er tremble in the gale, yet tremble still,
Fanned by the water-fall ! and there my friends
Behold the dark green file of long lank weeds,*
That all at once (a most fantastic sight !)
Still nod and drip beneath the dripping edge
Of the blue clay-stone.

               Now, my friends emerge
Beneath the wide wide Heaven—and view again
The many-steepled tract magnificent
Of hilly fields and meadows, and the sea,
With some fair bark, perhaps, whose sails light up

* *Of long lank weeds.* The *Asplenium scolopendrium,* called in some countries the Adder's Tongue, in others the Hart's Tongue : but Withering gives the Adder's Tongue as the trivial name of the *Ophioglossum* only.

The slip of smooth clear blue betwixt two Isles
Of purple shadow ! Yes ! they wander on
In gladness all ; but thou, methinks, most glad,
My gentle-hearted Charles ! for thou hast pined
And hungered after Nature, many a year,
In the great City pent, winning thy way
With sad yet patient soul, through evil and pain
And strange calamity ! Ah ! slowly sink
Behind the western ridge, thou glorious sun !
Shine in the slant beams of the sinking orb,
Ye purple heath-flowers ! richlier burn, ye clouds !
Live in the yellow light, ye distant groves !
And kindle, thou blue ocean ! So my Friend
Struck with deep joy may stand, as I have stood,
Silent with swimming sense ; yea, gazing round
On the wide landscape, gaze till all doth seem
Less gross than bodily ; and of such hues
As veil the Almighty Spirit, when yet he makes
Spirits perceive his presence.

                              A delight
Comes sudden on my heart, and I am glad
As I myself were there ! Nor in this bower,
This little lime-tree bower, have I not marked
Much that has soothed me. Pale beneath the blaze
Hung the transparent foliage ; and I watched
Some broad and sunny leaf, and loved to see
The shadow of the leaf and stem above
Dappling its sunshine ! And that walnut-tree
Was richly tinged, and a deep radiance lay
Full on the ancient ivy, which usurps
Those fronting elms, and now, with blackest mass
Makes their dark branches gleam a lighter hue
Through the late twilight : and though now the bat
Wheels silent by, and not a swallow twitters,
Yet still the solitary humble-bee
Sings in the bean-flower ! Henceforth I shall know
That Nature ne'er deserts the wise and pure ;

No plot so narrow, be but Nature there,
No waste so vacant, but may well employ
Each faculty of sense, and keep the heart
Awake to Love and Beauty ! and sometimes
'Tis well to be bereft of promised good,
That we may lift the Soul, and contemplate
With lively joy the joys we cannot share.
My gentle-hearted Charles ! when the last rook
Beat its straight path along the dusky air
Homewards, I blest it ! deeming its black wing
(Now a dim speck, now vanishing in light)
Had crossed the mighty orb's dilated glory,
While thou stood'st gazing ; or when all was still,
Flew creeking * o'er thy head, and had a charm
For thee, my gentle-hearted Charles, to whom
No sound is dissonant which tells of Life.

Frost at Midnight

THE frost performs its secret ministry,
Unhelped by any wind. The owlet's cry
Came loud—and hark, again ! loud as before.
The inmates of my cottage, all at rest,
Have left me to that solitude, which suits
Abstruser musings : save that at my side
My cradled infant slumbers peacefully.
'Tis calm indeed ! so calm, that it disturbs
And vexes meditation with its strange
And extreme silentness. Sea, hill, and wood,
This populous village ! Sea, and hill, and wood,
With all the numberless goings on of life,

---

* *Flew creeking.* Some months after I had written this line, it
gave me pleasure to find that Bartram had observed the same cir-
cumstance of the Savanna Crane. " When these birds move their
wings in flight, their strokes are slow, moderate, and regular ; and
even when at a considerable distance or high above us, we plainly
hear the quill feathers ; their shafts and webs upon one another creek
as the joints or working of a vessel in a tempestuous sea.

Inaudible as dreams ! the thin blue flame
Lies on my low-burnt fire, and quivers not ;
Only that film, which fluttered on the grate,
Still flutters there, the sole unquiet thing.
Methinks, its motion in this hush of nature
Gives it dim sympathies with me who live,
Making it a companionable form,
Whose puny flaps and freaks the idling Spirit
By its own moods interprets, everywhere
Echo or mirror seeking of itself,
And makes a toy of Thought.

                    But O ! how oft,
How oft, at school, with most believing mind,
Presageful, have I gazed upon the bars,
To watch that fluttering stranger ! and as oft,
With unclosed lids, already had I dreamt
Of my sweet birth-place, and the old church-tower,
Whose bells, the poor man's only music, rang
From morn to evening, all the hot Fair-day,
So sweetly, that they stirred and haunted me
With a wild pleasure, falling on mine ear
Most like articulate sounds of things to come !
So gazed I, till the soothing things I dreamt
Lulled me to sleep, and sleep prolonged my dreams
And so I brooded all the following morn,
Awed by the stern preceptor's face, mine eye
Fixed with mock study on my swimming book :
Save if the door half opened, and I snatched
A hasty glance, and still my heart leaped up,
For still I hoped to see the stranger's face,
Townsman, or aunt, or sister more beloved,
My play-mate when we both were clothed alike !

Dear Babe, that sleepest cradled by my side,
Whose gentle breathings, heard in this deep calm,
Fill up the interspersed vacancies
And momentary pauses of the thought !

My babe so beautiful ! it thrills my heart
With tender gladness, thus to look at thee,
And think that thou shalt learn far other lore
And in far other scenes ! For I was reared
In the great city, pent 'mid cloisters dim,
And saw nought lovely but the sky and stars.
But thou, my babe ! shalt wander like a breeze
By lakes and sandy shores, beneath the crags
Of ancient mountain, and beneath the clouds,
Which image in their bulk both lakes and shores
And mountain crags ; so shalt thou see and hear
The lovely shapes and sounds intelligible
Of that eternal language, which thy God
Utters, who from eternity doth teach
Himself in all, and all things in himself.
Great universal Teacher ! he shall mould
Thy spirit, and by giving make it ask.

Therefore all seasons shall be sweet to thee,
Whether the summer clothe the general earth
With greenness, or the redbreast sit and sing
Betwixt the tufts of snow on the bare branch
Of mossy apple-tree, while the nigh thatch
Smokes in the sun-thaw ; whether the eve-drops fall
Heard only in the trances of the blast,
Or if the secret ministry of frost
Shall hang them up in silent icicles,
Quietly shining to the quiet Moon.

Lines

*Written in the Album at Elbingerode, in the Hartz
Forest*

I STOOD on Brocken's * sovran height, and saw
Woods crowding upon woods, hills over hills,

* The highest mountain in the Hartz, and indeed in North Germany.

A surging scene, and only limited
By the blue distance. Heavily my way
Downward I dragged through fir groves evermore,
Where bright green moss heaves in sepulchral forms
Speckled with sunshine ; and, but seldom heard,
The sweet bird's song became a hollow sound ;
And the breeze, murmuring indivisibly,
Preserved its solemn murmur most distinct
From many a note of many a waterfall,
And the brook's chatter ; 'mid whose islet stones
The dingy kidling with its tinkling bell
Leaped frolicsome, or old romantic goat
Sat, his white beard slow waving. I moved on
In low and languid mood : * for I had found
That outward forms, the loftiest, still receive
Their finer influence from the Life within ;—
Fair cyphers else : fair, but of import vague
Or unconcerning, where the heart not finds
History or prophecy of friend, or child,
Or gentle maid, our first and early love,
Or father, or the venerable name
Of our adored country ! O thou Queen,
Thou delegated Deity of Earth,
O dear, dear England ! how my longing eye
Turned westward, shaping in the steady clouds
Thy sands and high white cliffs !

                  My native Land !
Filled with the thought of thee this heart was proud,
Yea, mine eye swam with tears ; that all the view
From sovran Brocken, woods and woody hills,
Floated away, like a departing dream,
Feeble and dim ! Stranger, these impulses

---

*   When I have gazed
  From some high eminence on goodly vales
  And cots and villages embowered below,
  The thought would rise that all to me was strange
  Amid the scenes so fair, nor one small spot
  Where my tired mind might rest, and call it home.
             SOUTHEY's *Hymn to the Penates.*

Blame thou not lightly ; nor will I profane,
With hasty judgment or injurious doubt,
That man's sublimer spirit, who can feel
That God is everywhere ! the God who framed
Mankind to be one mighty family,
Himself our Father, and the World our Home.

BIRD POEMS

BIRD POEMS BY WORDSWORTH

The Green Linnet

BENEATH these fruit-tree boughs that shed
Their snow-white blossoms on my head,
With brightest sunshine round me spread
    Of spring's unclouded weather,
In this sequestered nook how sweet
To sit upon my orchard-seat !
And birds and flowers once more to greet,
    My last year's friends together.

One have I marked, the happiest guest
In all this covert of the blest :
Hail to Thee, far above the rest
    In joy of voice and pinion !
Thou, Linnet ! in thy green array,
Presiding Spirit here to-day,
Dost lead the revels of the May ;
    And this is thy dominion.

While birds, and butterflies, and flowers,
Make all one band of paramours,
Thou, ranging up and down the bowers,
    Art sole in thy employment :
A Life, a Presence like the Air,
Scattering thy gladness without care,
Too blest with any one to pair ;
    Thyself thy own enjoyment.

Amid yon tuft of hazel trees
That twinkle to the gusty breeze,
Behold him perched in ecstasies,
    Yet seeming still to hover ;
There ! where the flutter of his wings
Upon his back and body flings
Shadows and sunny glimmerings,
    That cover him all over.

My dazzled sight he oft deceives,
A Brother of the dancing leaves ;
Then flits, and from the cottage-eaves
    Pours forth his song in gushes ;
As if by that exulting strain
He mocked and treated with disdain
The voiceless Form he chose to feign,
    While fluttering in the bushes.

To a Sky-lark

Up with me ! up with me into the clouds !
    For thy song, Lark, is strong ;
Up with me, up with me into the clouds !
    Singing, singing,
With clouds and sky about thee ringing,
    Lift me, guide me till I find
That spot which seems so to thy mind !

I have walked through wildernesses dreary
And to-day my heart is weary ;
Had I now the wings of a Faery,
    Up to thee would I fly.
There is madness about thee, and joy divine
    In that song of thine ;
Lift me, guide me high and high
To thy banqueting-place in the sky.

Joyous as morning
Thou art laughing and scorning ;
Thou hast a nest for thy love and thy rest,
And, though little troubled with sloth,
Drunken Lark ! thou would'st be loth
To be such a traveller as I.
Happy, happy Liver,
With a soul as strong as a mountain river
Pouring out praise to the Almighty Giver,
    Joy and jollity be with us both !

Alas ! my journey, rugged and uneven,
Through prickly moors or dusty ways must wind ;
But hearing thee, or others of thy kind,
As full of gladness and as free of heaven,
I, with my fate contented, will plod on,
And hope for higher raptures, when life's day is done.

To a Sky-lark

ETHEREAL minstrel ! pilgrim of the sky !
Dost thou despise the earth where cares abound ?
Or, while the wings aspire, are heart and eye
Both with thy nest upon the dewy ground ?
Thy nest which thou canst drop into at will,
Those quivering wings composed, that music still !
Leave to the nightingale her shady wood ;
A privacy of glorious light is thine ;
Whence thou dost pour upon the world a flood
Of harmony, with instinct more divine ;
Type of the wise who soar, but never roam ;
True to the kindred points of Heaven and Home !

" O Nightingale ! thou surely art "

O NIGHTINGALE ! thou surely art
A creature of a " fiery heart " :—
These notes of thine—they pierce and pierce ;
Tumultuous harmony and fierce !
Thou sing'st as if the God of wine
Had helped thee to a Valentine ;
A song in mockery and despite
Of shades, and dews, and silent night ;
And steady bliss, and all the loves
Now sleeping in these peaceful groves.

I heard a Stock-dove sing or say
His homely tale, this very day ;
His voice was buried among trees,
Yet to be come at by the breeze :
He did not cease ; but cooed—and cooed ;
And somewhat pensively he wooed :
He sang of love, with quiet blending,
Slow to begin, and never ending ;
Of serious faith, and inward glee ;
That was the song—the song for me !

To the Cuckoo

O BLITHE New-comer ! I have heard,
I hear thee and rejoice,
O Cuckoo ! shall I call thee Bird,
Or but a wandering Voice ?

While I am lying on the grass
Thy twofold shout I hear,
From hill to hill it seems to pass,
At once far off, and near.

Though babbling only to the Vale,
Of sunshine and of flowers,
Thou bringest unto me a tale
Of visionary hours.

Thrice welcome, darling of the Spring !
Even yet thou art to me
No bird, but an invisible thing,
A voice, a mystery ;

The same whom in my school-boy days
I listened to ; that Cry
Which made me look a thousand ways
In bush, and tree, and sky.

To seek thee did I often rove
Through woods and on the green ;
And thou wert still a hope, a love ;
Still longed for, never seen.

And I can listen to thee yet ;
Can lie upon the plain
And listen, till I do beget
That golden time again.

O blessed Bird ! the earth we pace
Again appears to be
An unsubstantial, faery place ;
That is fit home for Thee !

BIRD POEMS BY COLERIDGE

To the Nightingale

SISTER of love-lorn poets, Philomel !
How many bards in city garret pent,
While at their window they with downward eye
Mark the faint lamp-beam on the kennelled mud,
And listen to the drowsy cry of watchmen
(Those hoarse unfeathered nightingales of time !),
How many wretched bards address *thy* name,
And hers, the full-orbed queen that shines above.
But I *do* hear thee, and the high bough mark,
Within whose mild moon-mellowed foliage hid
Thou warblest sad thy pity-pleading strains.
Oh ! I have listened, till my working soul,
Waked by those strains to thousand phantasies,
Absorbed hath ceased to listen ! Therefore oft,
I hymn thy name : and with a proud delight
Oft will I tell thee, minstrel of the moon !
" Most musical, most melancholy " bird !
That all thy soft diversities of tone,
Tho' sweeter far than the delicious airs
That vibrate from a white-arm'd lady's harp.
What time the languishment of lonely love
Melts in her eye, and heaves her breast of snow,
Are not so sweet as is the voice of her,
My Sara—best beloved of human kind !
When breathing the pure soul of tenderness
She thrills me with the husband's promised name !

The Raven

A Christmas Tale, told by a School-Boy to his Little Brothers and Sisters

UNDERNEATH an old oak tree
There was of swine a huge company,
That grunted as they crunched the mast :
For that was ripe, and fell full fast.
Then they trotted away, for the wind grew high :
One acorn they left, and no more might you spy.
Next came a Raven, that liked not such folly :
He belonged, they did say, to the witch Melancholy !
Blacker was he than blackest jet,
Flew low in the rain, and his feathers not wet.
He picked up the acorn and buried it straight
By the side of a river both deep and great.
        Where then did the Raven go ?
        He went high and low,
Over hill, over dale, did the black Raven go.
        Many Autumns, many Springs,
        Travelled he with wandering wings :
        Many Summers, many Winters—
        I can't tell half his adventures.

At length he came back, and with him a She,
And the acorn was grown to a tall oak tree.
They built them a nest in the topmost bough,
And young ones they had, and were happy enow.
But soon came a woodman in leathern guise,
His brow, like a pent-house, hung over his eyes.
He'd an axe in his hand, not a word he spoke,
But with many a hem ! and a sturdy stroke,
At length he brought down the poor Raven's own oak.
His young ones were killed, for they could not depart,
And their mother did die of a broken heart.

The boughs from the trunk the woodman did sever ;
And they floated it down on the course of the river.
They sawed it in planks, and its bark they did strip,
And with this tree and others they made a good ship.
The ship, it was launched ; but in sight of the land
Such a storm there did rise as no ship could withstand.
It bulged on a rock, and the waves rushed in fast :
Round and round flew the Raven, and cawed to the
        blast.
He heard the last shriek of the perishing souls—
See ! See ! o'er the topmast the mad water rolls !
    Right glad was the Raven, and off he went fleet,
And Death riding home on a cloud he did meet,
And he thanked him again and again for this treat :
    They had taken his all, and Revenge it was sweet !

The Nightingale

A Conversation Poem. April 1798

No Cloud, no relique of the sunken day
Distinguishes the West, no long thin slip
Of sullen light, no obscure trembling hues.
Come, we will rest on this old mossy bridge !
You see the glimmer of the stream beneath,
But hear no murmuring : it flows silently,
O'er its soft bed of verdure.   All is still,
A balmy night ! and though the stars be dim,
Yet let us think upon the vernal showers
That gladden the green earth, and we shall find
A pleasure in the dimness of the stars.
And hark ! the Nightingale begins its song,
" Most musical, most melancholy " bird ! *

    * " *Most musical, most melancholy.*"   This passage in Milton pos-
sesses an excellence far superior to that of mere description.   It is
spoken in the character of the melancholy man, and has therefore a
dramatic propriety.   The Author makes this remark, to rescue
himself from the charge of having alluded with levity to a line in
Milton.

A melancholy bird ? Oh ! idle thought !
In Nature there is nothing melancholy.
But some night-wandering man whose heart was
    pierced
With the remembrance of a grievous wrong,
Or slow distemper, or neglected love,
(And so, poor wretch ! filled all things with himself,
And made all gentle sounds tell back the tale
Of his own sorrow,) he, and such as he,
First named these notes a melancholy strain.
And many a poet echoes the conceit ;
Poet who hath been building up the rhyme
When he had better far have stretched his limbs
Beside a brook in mossy forest-dell,
By sun or moon-light, to the influxes
Of shapes and sounds and shifting elements
Surrendering his whole spirit, of his song
And of his fame forgetful ! so his fame
Should share in Nature's immortality,
A venerable thing ! and so his song
Should make all Nature lovelier, and itself
Be loved like Nature ! But 'twill not be so ;
And youths and maidens most poetical,
Who lose the deepening twilights of the spring
In ball-rooms and hot theatres, they still
Full of meek sympathy must heave their sighs
O'er Philomela's pity-pleading strains.

    My Friend, and thou, our Sister ! we have learnt
A different lore : we may not thus profane
Nature's sweet voices, always full of love
And joyance ! 'Tis the merry Nightingale
That crowds, and hurries, and precipitates
With fast thick warble his delicious notes,
As he were fearful that an April night
Would be too short for him to utter forth
His love-chant, and disburthen his full soul
Of all its music !

And I know a grove
Of large extent, hard by a castle huge,
Which the great lord inhabits not ; and so
This grove is wild with tangling underwood,
And the trim walks are broken up, and grass,
Thin grass and king-cups grow within the paths.
But never elsewhere in one place I knew
So many nightingales ; and far and near,
In wood and thicket, over the wide grove,
They answer and provoke each other's song,
With skirmish and capricious passagings,
And murmurs musical and swift jug jug,
And one low piping sound more sweet than all—
Stirring the air with such a harmony,
That should you close your eyes, you might almost
Forget it was not day ! On moon-lit bushes,
Whose dewy leaflets are but half disclosed,
You may perchance behold them on the twigs,
Their bright, bright eyes, their eyes both bright and
       full,
Glistening, while many a glow-worm in the shade
Lights up her love-torch.

       A most gentle Maid,
Who dwelleth in her hospitable home
Hard by the castle, and at latest eve
(Even like a Lady vowed and dedicate
To something more than Nature in the grove)
Glides through the pathways ; she knows all their
       notes,
That gentle Maid ! and oft, a moment's space,
What time the moon was lost behind a cloud,
Hath heard a pause of silence ; till the moon
Emerging, hath awakened earth and sky
With one sensation, and these wakeful birds
Have all burst forth in choral minstrelsy,
As if some sudden gale had swept at once
A hundred airy harps ! And she hath watched

Many a nightingale perched giddily
On blossomy twig still swinging from the breeze,
And to that motion tune his wanton song
Like tipsy joy that reels with tossing head.

Farewell, O Warbler ! till to-morrow eve,
And you, my friends ! farewell, a short farewell !
We have been loitering long and pleasantly,
And now for our dear homes.—That strain again !
Full fain it would delay me ! My dear babe,
Who, capable of no articulate sound,
Mars all things with his imitative lisp,
How he would place his hand beside his ear,
His little hand, the small forefinger up,
And bid us listen ! And I deem it wise
To make him Nature's play-mate. He knows well
The evening-star ; and once, when he awoke
In most distressful mood (some inward pain
Had made up that strange thing, an infant's dream),
I hurried with him to our orchard plot,
And he beheld the moon, and, hushed at once,
Suspends his sobs, and laughs most silently,
While his fair eyes, that swam with undropped tears,
Did glitter in the yellow moon-beam ! Well !—
It is a father's tale : But if that Heaven
Should give me life, his childhood shall grow up
Familiar with these songs, that with the night
He may associate joy.—Once more, farewell,
Sweet Nightingale ! Once more, my friends ! fare-
well.

Answer to a Child's Question

Do you ask what the birds say ? The sparrow, the
dove,
The linnet and thrush say, " I love and I love ! "
In the winter they're silent—the wind is so strong :

What it says I don't know, but it sings a loud
    song.
But green leaves, and blossoms, and sunny warm
    weather,
And singing, and loving—all come back together.
But the lark is so brimful of gladness and love,
The green fields below him, the blue sky above,
That he sings, and he sings ; and for ever sings he—
" I love my Love, and my Love loves me ! "

A POEM OF RETRIBUTION BY
WORDSWORTH

Peter Bell

A Tale

What's in a *Name ?*

·   ·   ·   ·   ·   ·   ·   ·

Brutus will start a Spirit as soon as Cæsar !

To ROBERT SOUTHEY, Esq., P.L., etc., etc.

MY DEAR FRIEND,
        The Tale of Peter Bell, which I now introduce
to your notice, and to that of the Public, has, in its
Manuscript state, nearly survived its *minority ;*—for
it first saw the light in the summer of 1798. During
this long interval, pains have been taken at different
times to make the production less unworthy of a
favourable reception ; or, rather, to fit it for filling
permanently a station, however humble, in the Literature of our Country. This has, indeed, been the aim
of all my endeavours in Poetry, which, you know, have
been sufficiently laborious to prove that I deem the
Art not lightly to be approached ; and that the attain-
ment of excellence in it may laudably be made the
principal object of intellectual pursuit by any man,
who, with reasonable consideration of circumstances,
has faith in his own impulses.
    The Poem of Peter Bell, as the Prologue will show,

was composed under a belief that the Imagination not only does not require for its exercise the intervention of supernatural agency, but that, though such agency be excluded, the faculty may be called forth as imperiously and for kindred results of pleasure, by incidents, within the compass of poetic probability, in the humblest departments of daily life. Since that Prologue was written, *you* have exhibited most splendid effects of judicious daring, in the opposite and usual course. Let this acknowledgment make my peace with the lovers of the supernatural ; and I am persuaded it will be admitted, that to you, as a Master in that province of the Art, the following Tale, whether from contrast or congruity, is not an unappropriate offering. Accept it, then, as a public testimony of affectionate admiration from one with whose name yours has been often coupled (to use your own words) for evil and for good ; and believe me to be, with earnest wishes that life and health may be granted you to complete the many important works in which you are engaged, and with high respect, most faithfully yours, WILLIAM WORDSWORTH.

Rydal Mount, April 7, 1819.

PROLOGUE

THERE's something in a flying horse,
There's something in a huge balloon ;
But through the clouds I'll never float
Until I have a little Boat,
Shaped like the crescent-moon.

And now I *have* a little Boat,
In shape a very crescent-moon.
Fast through the clouds my boat can sail ;
But if perchance your faith should fail,
Look up—and you shall see me soon !

The woods, my Friends, are round you roaring,
Rocking and roaring like a sea ;
The noise of danger's in your ears,
And ye have all a thousand fears
Both for my little Boat and me !

Meanwhile untroubled I admire
The pointed horns of my canoe ;
And, did not pity touch my breast,
To see how ye are all distrest,
Till my ribs ached, I'd laugh at you !

Away we go, my Boat and I—
Frail man ne'er sate in such another ;
Whether among the winds we strive,
Or deep into the clouds we dive,
Each is contented with the other.

Away we go—and what care we
For treasons, tumults, and for wars ?
We are as calm in our delight
As is the crescent-moon so bright
Among the scattered stars.

Up goes my Boat among the stars
Through many a breathless field of light,
Through many a long blue field of ether,
Leaving ten thousand stars beneath her :
Up goes my little Boat so bright !

The Crab, the Scorpion, and the Bull—
We pry among them all ; have shot
High o'er the red-haired race of Mars,
Covered from top to toe with scars ;
Such company I like it not !

The towns in Saturn are decayed,
And melancholy Spectres throng them ;—

The Pleiads, that appear to kiss
Each other in the vast abyss,
With joy I sail among them.

Swift Mercury resounds with mirth,
Great Jove is full of stately bowers ;
But these, and all that they contain,
What are they to that tiny grain,
That little Earth of ours ?

Then back to Earth, the dear green Earth :—
Whole ages if I here should roam,
The world for my remarks and me
Would not a whit the better be ;
I've left my heart at home.

See ! there she is, the matchless Earth !
There spreads the famed Pacific Ocean !
Old Andes thrusts yon craggy spear
Through the grey clouds ; the Alps are here,
Like waters in commotion !

Yon tawny slip is Libya's sands ;
That silver thread the river Dnieper ;
And look, where clothed in brightest green
Is a sweet Isle, of isles the Queen ;
Ye fairies, from all evil keep her !

And see the town where I was born !
Around those happy fields we span
In boyish gambols ;—I was lost
Where I have been, but on this coast
I feel I am a man.

Never did fifty things at once
Appear so lovely, never, never ;—
How tunefully the forests ring !
To hear the earth's soft murmuring
Thus could I hang for ever !

" Shame on you ! " cried my little Boat,
" Was ever such a homesick Loon,
Within a living Boat to sit,
And make no better use of it ;
A Boat twin-sister of the crescent-moon !

" Ne'er in the breast of full-grown Poet
Fluttered so faint a heart before ;—
Was it the music of the spheres
That overpowered your mortal ears ?
—Such din shall trouble them no more.

" These nether precincts do not lack
Charms of their own ;—then come with me ;
I want a comrade, and for you
There's nothing that I would not do ;
Nought is there that you shall not see.

" Haste ! and above Siberian snows
We'll sport amid the boreal morning ;
Will mingle with her lustres gliding
Among the stars, the stars now hiding,
And now the stars adorning.

" I know the secrets of a land
Where human foot did never stray ;
Fair is that land as evening skies,
And cool, though in the depth it lies
Of burning Africa.

" Or we'll into the realm of Faery,
Among the lovely shades of things ;
The shadowy forms of mountains bare,
And streams, and bowers, and ladies fair
The shades of palaces and kings !

" Or, if you thirst with hardy zeal
Less quiet regions to explore,
Prompt voyage shall to you reveal

How earth and heaven are taught to feel
The might of magic lore ! ''

" My little vagrant Form of light,
My gay and beautiful Canoe,
Well have you played your friendly part ;
As kindly take what from my heart
Experience forces—then adieu !

" Temptation lurks among your words ;
But, while these pleasures you're pursuing
Without impediment or let,
No wonder if you quite forget
What on the earth is doing.

" There was a time when all mankind
Did listen with a faith sincere
To tuneful tongues in mystery versed ;
Then Poets fearlessly rehearsed
The wonders of a wild career.

" Go—(but the world's a sleepy world,
And 'tis, I fear, an age too late)
Take with you some ambitious Youth !
For, restless Wanderer ! I, in truth,
Am all unfit to be your mate.

" Long have I loved what I behold,
The night that calms, the day that cheers ;
The common growth of mother-earth
Suffices me—her tears, her mirth,
Her humblest mirth and tears.

" The dragon's wing, the magic ring,
I shall not covet for my dower,
If I along that lowly way
With sympathetic heart may stray,
And with a soul of power.

" These given, what more need I desire
To stir, to soothe, or elevate ?
What nobler marvels than the mind
May in life's daily prospect find,
May find or there create ?

" A potent wand doth Sorrow wield ;
What spell so strong as guilty Fear !
Repentance is a tender Sprite ;
If aught on earth have heavenly might,
'Tis lodged within her silent tear.

" But grant my wishes,—let us now
Descend from this ethereal height ;
Then take thy way, adventurous Skiff,
More daring far than Hippogriff,
And be thy own delight !

" To the stone-table in my garden,
Loved haunt of many a summer hour,
The Squire is come : his daughter Bess
Beside him in the cool recess
Sits blooming like a flower.

" With these are many more convened ;
They know not I have been so far ;—
I see them there, in number nine,
Beneath the spreading Weymouth-pine !
I see them—there they are !

" There sits the Vicar and his Dame ;
And there my good friend, Stephen Otter ;
And, ere the light of evening fail,
To them I must relate the Tale
Of Peter Bell the Potter."

Off flew the Boat—away she flees,
Spurning her freight with indignation !
And I, as well as I was able

On two poor legs, toward my stone-table
Limped on with sore vexation.

" O, here he is ! " cried little Bess—
She saw me at the garden door ;
" We've waited anxiously and long,"
They cried, and all around me throng,
Full nine of them or more !

" Reproach me not—your fears be still—
Be thankful we again have met ;—
Resume, my Friends ! within the shade
Your seats, and quickly shall be paid
The well-remembered debt."

I spake with faltering voice, like one
Not wholly rescued from the pale
Of a wild dream, or worse illusion ;
But, straight, to cover my confusion,
Began the promised Tale.

PART FIRST

ALL by the moonlight river side
Groaned the poor Beast—alas ! in vain ;
The staff was raised to loftier height,
And the blows fell with heavier weight
As Peter struck—and struck again.

" Hold ! " cried the Squire, " against the rules
Of common sense you're surely sinning ;
This leap is for us all too bold ;
Who Peter was, let that be told,
And start from the beginning."

——" A Potter,* Sir, he was by trade,"
Said I, becoming quite collected ;

* In the dialect of the North, a hawker of earthenware is thus
designated.

" And wheresoever he appeared,
Full twenty times was Peter feared
For once that Peter was respected.

" He, two-and-thirty years or more,
Had been a wild and woodland rover ;
Had heard the Atlantic surges roar
On farthest Cornwall's rocky shore,
And trod the cliffs of Dover.

" And he had seen Caernarvon's towers,
And well he knew the spire of Sarum ;
And he had been where Lincoln bell
Flings o'er the fen that ponderous knell—
A far-renowned alarum !

" At Doncaster, at York, and Leeds,
And merry Carlisle had he been ;
And all along the Lowlands fair,
All through the bonny shire of Ayr ;
And far as Aberdeen.

" And he had been at Inverness ;
And Peter, by the mountain-rills,
Had danced his round with Highland lassies ;
And he had lain beside his asses
On lofty Cheviot Hills :

" And he had trudged through Yorkshire dales,
Among the rocks and winding *scars ;*
Where deep and low the hamlets lie
Beneath their little patch of sky
And little lot of stars :

" And all along the indented coast,
Bespattered with the salt-sea foam ;
Where'er a knot of houses lay
On headland, or in hollow bay ;—
Sure never man like him did roam !

" As well might Peter, in the Fleet,
Have been fast bound, a begging debtor ;—
He travelled here, he travelled there ;—
But not the value of a hair
Was heart or head the better.

" He roved among the vales and streams,
In the green wood and hollow dell ;
They were his dwellings night and day,—
But nature ne'er could find the way
Into the heart of Peter Bell.

" In vain, through every changeful year,
Did Nature lead him as before ;
A primrose by a river's brim
A yellow primrose was to him,
And it was nothing more.

" Small change it made on Peter's heart
To see his gentle panniered train
With more than vernal pleasure feeding,
Where'er the tender grass was leading
Its earliest green along the lane.

" In vain, through water, earth, and air,
The soul of happy sound was spread,
When Peter on some April morn,
Beneath the broom or budding thorn,
Made the warm earth his lazy bed.

" At noon, when, by the forest's edge,
He lay beneath the branches high,
The soft blue sky did never melt
Into his heart ; he never felt
The witchery of the soft blue sky !

" On a fair prospect some have looked
And felt, as I have heard them say,

As if the moving time had been
A thing as steadfast as the scene
On which they gazed themselves away.

" Within the breast of Peter Bell
The silent raptures found no place
He was a Carl as wild and rude
As ever hue-and-cry pursued,
As ever ran a felon's race.

" Of all that lead a lawless life,
Of all that love their lawless lives,
In city or in village small,
He was the wildest far of all ;—
He had a dozen wedded wives.

" Nay, start not !—wedded wives—and twelve
But how one wife could e'er come near him,
In simple truth I cannot tell ;
For, be it said of Peter Bell,
To see him was to fear him.

" Though Nature could not touch his heart
By lovely forms, and silent weather,
And tender sounds, yet you might see
At once, that Peter Bell and she
Had often been together.

" A savage wildness round him hung
As of a dweller out of doors ;
In his whole figure and his mien
A savage character was seen
Of mountains and of dreary moors.

" To all the unshaped half-human thoughts
Which solitary Nature feeds
'Mid summer storms or winter's ice,
Had Peter joined whatever vice
The cruel city breeds.

" His face was keen as is the wind
That cuts along the hawthorn-fence ;—
Of courage you saw little there,
But, in its stead, a medley air
Of cunning and of impudence.

" He had a dark and sidelong walk,
And long and slouching was his gait ;
Beneath his looks so bare and bold,
You might perceive, his spirit cold
Was playing with some inward bait.

" His forehead wrinkled was and furred ;
A work, one half of which was done
By thinking of his ' whens ' and ' hows ; '
And half, by knitting of his brows
Beneath the glaring sun.

" There was a hardness in his cheek,
There was a hardness in his eye,
As if the man had fixed his face,
In many a solitary place,
Against the wind and open sky ! "

ONE NIGHT, (and now my little Bess !
We've reached at last the promised Tale :)
One beautiful November night,
When the full moon was shining bright
Upon the rapid river Swale,

Along the river's winding banks
Peter was travelling all alone ;—
Whether to buy or sell, or led
By pleasure running in his head,
To me was never known.

He trudged along through copse and brake,
He trudged along o'er hill and dale ;

Nor for the moon cared he a tittle,
And for the stars he cared as little,
And for the murmuring river Swale.

But, chancing to espy a path
That promised to cut short the way
As many a wiser man hath done,
He left a trusty guide for one
That might his steps betray.

To a thick wood he soon is brought
Where cheerily his course he weaves,
And whistling loud may yet be heard,
Though often buried, like a bird
Darkling, among the boughs and leaves.

But quickly Peter's mood is changed,
And on he drives with cheeks that burn
In downright fury and in wrath ;—
There's little sign the treacherous path
Will to the road return !

The path grows dim, and dimmer still ;
Now up, now down, the Rover wends,
With all the sail that he can carry,
Till brought to a deserted quarry—
And there the pathway ends.

He paused—for shadows of strange shape,
Massy and black, before him lay ;
But through the dark, and through the cold,
And through the yawning fissures old,
Did Peter boldly press his way

Right through the quarry ;—and behold
A scene of soft and lovely hue !
Where blue and grey, and tender green,
Together make as sweet a scene
As ever human eye did view.

Beneath the clear blue sky he saw
A little field of meadow ground ;
But field or meadow name it not ;
Call it of earth a small green plot,
With rocks encompassed round.

The Swale flowed under the grey rocks,
But he flowed quiet and unseen ;—
You need a strong and stormy gale
To bring the noises of the Swale
To that green spot, so calm and green !

And is there no one dwelling here,
No hermit with his beads and glass ?
And does no little cottage look
Upon this soft and fertile nook ?
Does no one live near this green grass ?

Across the deep and quiet spot
Is Peter driving through the grass—
And now has reached the skirting trees ;
When, turning round his head, he sees
A solitary Ass.

" A Prize ! " cries Peter—but he first
Must spy about him far and near :
There's not a single house in sight,
No woodman's hut, no cottage light—
Peter, you need not fear !

There's nothing to be seen but woods,
And rocks that spread a hoary gleam,
And this one Beast, that from the bed
Of the green meadow hangs his head
Over the silent stream.

His head is with a halter bound ;
The halter seizing, Peter leapt
Upon the Creature's back, and plied

With ready heels his shaggy side ;
But still the Ass his station kept.

Then Peter gave a sudden jerk,
A jerk that from a dungeon-floor
Would have pulled up an iron ring ;
But still the heavy-headed Thing
Stood just as he had stood before !

Quoth Peter, leaping from his seat,
" There is some plot against me laid ; "
Once more the little meadow-ground
And all the hoary cliffs around
He cautiously surveyed.

All, all is silent—rocks and woods,
All still and silent—far and near !
Only the Ass, with motion dull,
Upon the pivot of his skull
Turns round his long left ear.

Thought Peter, What can mean all this ?
Some ugly witchcraft must be here !
—Once more the Ass, with motion dull,
Upon the pivot of his skull
Turned round his long left ear.

Suspicion ripened into dread ;
Yet with deliberate action slow,
His staff high-raising, in the pride
Of skill, upon the sounding hide,
He dealt a sturdy blow.

The poor Ass staggered with the shock ;
And then, as if to take his ease,
In quiet uncomplaining mood,
Upon the spot where he had stood,
Dropped gently down upon his knees :

As gently on his side he fell ;
And by the river's brink did lie ;
And, while he lay like one that mourned,
The patient Beast on Peter turned
His shining hazel eye.

'Twas but one mild, reproachful look,
A look more tender than severe ;
And straight in sorrow, not in dread,
He turned the eye-ball in his head
Towards the smooth river deep and clear.

Upon the Beast the sapling rings ;
His lank sides heaved, his limbs they stirred ;
He gave a groan, and then another,
Of that which went before the brother,
And then he gave a third.

All by the moonlight river side
He gave three miserable groans ;
And not till now hath Peter seen
How gaunt the Creature is,—how lean
And sharp his staring bones !

With legs stretched out and stiff he lay :—
No word of kind commiseration
Fell at the sight from Peter's tongue ;
With hard contempt his heart was wrung,
With hatred and vexation.

The meagre beast lay still as death ;
And Peter's lips with fury quiver ;
Quoth he, " You little mulish dog,
I'll fling your carcase like a log
Head-foremost down the river ! "

An impious oath confirmed the threat—
Whereat from the earth on which he lay

To all the echoes, south and north,
And east and west, the Ass sent forth
A long and clamorous bray !

This outcry, on the heart of Peter,
Seems like a note of joy to strike,—
Joy at the heart of Peter knocks ;
But in the echo of the rocks
Was something Peter did not like.

Whether to cheer his coward breast,
Or that he could not break the chain,
In this serene and solemn hour,
Twined round him by demoniac power,
To the blind work he turned again.

Among the rocks and winding crags ;
Among the mountains far away ;
Once more the ass did lengthen out
More ruefully a deep-drawn shout,
The hard dry see-saw of his horrible bray !

What is there now in Peter's heart !
Or whence the might of this strange sound ?
The moon uneasy looked and dimmer,
The broad blue heavens appeared to glimmer,
And the rocks staggered all around—

From Peter's hand the sapling dropped !
Threat has he none to execute ;
" If any one should come and see
That I am here, they'll think," quoth he,
" I'm helping this poor dying brute."

He scans the Ass from limb to limb,
And ventures now to uplift his eyes ;
More steady looks the moon, and clear,
More like themselves the rocks appear
And touch more quiet skies.

His scorn returns—his hate revives ;
He stoops the Ass's neck to seize
With malice—that again takes flight ;
For in the pool a startling sight
Meets him, among the inverted trees.

Is it the moon's distorted face ?
The ghost-like image of a cloud ?
Is it a gallows there portrayed ?
Is Peter of himself afraid ?
Is it a coffin,—or a shroud ?

A grisly idol hewn in stone ?
Or imp from witch's lap let fall ?
Perhaps a ring of shining fairies ?
Such as pursue their feared vagaries
In sylvan bower, or haunted hall ?

Is it a fiend that to a stake
Of fire his desperate self is tethering ?
Or stubborn spirit doomed to yell
In solitary ward or cell,
Ten thousand miles from all his brethren ?

Never did pulse so quickly throb,
And never heart so loudly panted ;
He looks, he cannot choose but look ;
Like some one reading in a book—
A book that is enchanted.

Ah, well-a-day for Peter Bell !
He will be turned to iron soon,
Meet Statue for the court of Fear !
His hat is up—and every hair
Bristles, and whitens in the moon !

He looks, he ponders, looks again ;
He sees a motion—hears a groan ;

His eyes will burst—his heart will break—
He gives a loud and frightful shriek,
And back he falls, as if his life were flown !

PART SECOND

WE left our Hero in a trance,
Beneath the alders, near the river ;
The Ass is by the river-side,
And, where the feeble breezes glide,
Upon the stream the moonbeams quiver.

A happy respite ! but at length
He feels the glimmering of the moon ;
Wakes with glazed eye, and feebly sighing—
To sink, perhaps, where he is lying,
Into a second swoon !

He lifts his head, he sees his staff ;
He touches—'tis to him a treasure !
Faint recollection seems to tell
That he is yet where mortals dwell—
A thought received with languid pleasure !

His head upon his elbow propped,
Becoming less and less perplexed,
Sky-ward he looks—to rock and wood—
And then—upon the glassy flood
His wandering eye is fixed.

Thought he, that is the face of one
In his last sleep securely bound !
So toward the stream his head he bent,
And downward thrust his staff, intent
The river's depth to sound.

Now—like a tempest-shattered bark,
That overwhelmed and prostrate lies,
(2,604)

8

And in a moment to the verge
Is lifted of a foaming surge—
Full suddenly the Ass doth rise !

His staring bones all shake with joy,
And close by Peter's side he stands :
While Peter o'er the river bends,
The little Ass his neck extends,
And fondly licks his hands.

Such life is in the Ass's eyes,
Such life is in his limbs and ears ;
That Peter Bell, if he had been
The veriest coward ever seen,
Must now have thrown aside his fears.

The Ass looks on—and to his work
Is Peter quietly resigned ;
He touches here—he touches there—
And now among the dead man's hair
His sapling Peter has entwined.

He pulls—and looks—and pulls again ;
And he whom the poor Ass had lost,
The man who had been four days dead,
Head-foremost from the river's bed
Uprises like a ghost !

And Peter draws him to dry land ;
And through the brain of Peter pass
Some poignant twitches, fast and faster ;
" No doubt," quoth he, " he is the Master
Of this poor miserable Ass ! "

The meagre Shadow that looks on—
What would he now ? what is he doing ?
His sudden fit of joy is flown,—
He on his knees hath laid him down,
As if he were his grief renewing :

But no—that Peter on his back
Must mount, he shows well as he can :
Thought Peter then, come weal or woe,
I'll do what he would have me do,
In pity to this poor drowned man.

With that resolve he boldly mounts
Upon the pleased and thankful Ass ;
And then, without a moment's stay,
That earnest Creature turned away,
Leaving the body on the grass.

Intent upon his faithful watch,
The Beast four days and nights had past ;
A sweeter meadow ne'er was seen,
And there the Ass four days had been,
Nor ever once did break his fast :

Yet firm his step, and stout his heart ;
The mead is crossed—the quarry's mouth
Is reached ; but there the trusty guide
Into a thicket turns aside,
And deftly ambles towards the south.

When hark a burst of doleful sound !
And Peter honestly might say,
The like came never to his ears,
Though he has been, full thirty years,
A rover—night and day !

'Tis not a plover of the moors,
'Tis not a bittern of the fen ;
Nor can it be a barking fox,
Nor night-bird chambered in the rocks,
Nor wild-cat in a woody glen !

The Ass is startled—and stops short
Right in the middle of the thicket ;

And Peter, wont to whistle loud
Whether alone or in a crowd,
Is silent as a silent cricket.

What ails you now, my little Bess ?
Well may you tremble and look grave !
This cry—that rings along the wood,
This cry—that floats adown the flood,
Comes from the entrance of a cave :

I see a blooming Wood-boy there,
And if I had the power to say
How sorrowful the wanderer is,
Your heart would be as sad as his
Till you had kissed his tears away !

Grasping a hawthorn branch in hand,
All bright with berries ripe and red,
Into the cavern's mouth he peeps ;
Thence back into the moonlight creeps ;
Whom seeks he—whom ?—the silent dead.

His father !—Him doth he require—
Him hath he sought with fruitless pains,
Among the rocks, behind the trees ;
Now creeping on his hands and knees,
Now running o'er the open plains.

And hither is he come at last,
When he through such a day has gone,
By this dark cave to be distrest
Like a poor bird—her plundered nest
Hovering around with dolorous moan !

Of that intense and piercing cry
The listening Ass conjectures well ;
Wild as it is, he there can read
Some intermingled notes that plead
With touches irresistible.

But Peter—when he saw the Ass
Not only stop but turn, and change
The cherished tenor of his pace
That lamentable cry to chase—
It wrought in him conviction strange :

A faith that, for the dead man's sake
And this poor slave who loved him well,
Vengeance upon his head will fall,
Some visitation worse than all
Which ever till this night befell.

Meanwhile the Ass to reach his home,
Is striving stoutly as he may ;
But, while he climbs the woody hill,
The cry grows weak—and weaker still ;
And now at last it dies away.

So with his freight the Creature turns
Into a gloomy grove of beech,
Along the shade with footsteps true
Descending slowly, till the two
The open moonlight reach.

And there, along the narrow dell,
A fair smooth pathway you discern.
A length of green and open road—
As if it from a fountain flowed—
Winding away between the fern.

The rocks that tower on either side
Build up a wild fantastic scene ;
Temples like those among the Hindoos,
And mosques, and spires, and abbey windows,
And castles all with ivy green !

And, while the Ass pursues his way,
Along this solitary dell,

As pensively his steps advance,
The mosques and spires change countenance
And look at Peter Bell !

That unintelligible cry
Hath left him high in preparation,—
Convinced that he, or soon or late,
This very night will meet his fate—
And so he sits in expectation !

The strenuous Animal hath clomb
With the green path ; and now he wends
Where, shining like the smoothest sea,
In undisturbed immensity
A level plain extends.

But whence this faintly-rustling sound
By which the journeying pair are chased ?
—A withered leaf is close behind,
Light plaything for the sportive wind
Upon that solitary waste.

When Peter spied the moving thing,
It only doubled his distress ;
" Where there is not a bush or tree,
The very leaves they follow me—
So huge hath been my wickedness ! "

To a close lane they now are come,
Where, as before, the enduring Ass
Moves on without a moment's stop,
Nor once turns round his head to crop
A bramble-leaf or blade of grass.

Between the hedges as they go,
The white dust sleeps upon the lane ;
And Peter, ever and anon
Back-looking, sees, upon a stone,
Or in the dust, a crimson stain.

A stain—as of a drop of blood
By moonlight made more faint and wan ;
Ha ! why these sinkings of despair ?
He knows not how the blood comes there—
And Peter is a wicked man.

At length he spies a bleeding wound,
Where he had struck the Ass's head ;
He sees the blood, knows what it is,—
A glimpse of sudden joy was his,
But then it quickly fled ;

Of him whom sudden death had seized
He thought,—of thee, O faithful Ass !
And once again those ghastly pains
Shoot to and fro through heart and reins,
And through his brain like lightning pass.

PART THIRD

I'VE heard of one, a gentle Soul,
Though given to sadness and to gloom,
And for the fact will vouch,—one night
It chanced that by a taper's light
This man was reading in his room ;

Bending, as you or I might bend
At night o'er any pious book.
When sudden blackness overspread
The snow-white page on which he read,
And made the good man round him look.

The chamber walls were dark all round,—
And to his book he turned again ;
—The light had left the lonely taper,
And formed itself upon the paper
Into large letters—bright and plain !

The godly book was in his hand—
And, on the page, more black than coal,
Appeared, set forth in strange array,
A *word*—which to his dying day
Perplexed the good man's gentle soul.

The ghostly word, thus plainly seen,
Did never from his lips depart ;
But he hath said, poor gentle wight !
It brought full many a sin to light
Out of the bottom of his heart.

Dread Spirits ! to confound the meek
Why wander from your course so far,
Disordering colour, form, and stature !
—Let good men feel the soul of nature,
And see things as they are.

Yet, potent Spirits ! well I know,
How ye, that play with soul and sense,
Are not unused to trouble friends
Of goodness, for most gracious ends—
And this I speak in reverence !

But might I give advice to you,
Whom in my fear I love so well ;
From men of pensive virtue go,
Dread Beings ! and your empire show
On hearts like that of Peter Bell.

Your presence often have I felt
In darkness and the stormy night ;
And, with like force, if need there be,
Ye can put forth your agency
When earth is calm, and heaven is bright.

Then, coming from the wayward world,
That powerful world in which ye dwell,

Come, Spirits of the Mind ! and try
To-night, beneath the moonlight sky,
What may be done with Peter Bell !

—O, would that some more skilful voice
My further labour might prevent !
Kind Listeners, that around me sit,
I feel that I am all unfit
For such high argument.

I've played, I've danced, with my narration ;
I loitered long ere I began :
Ye waited then on my good pleasure ;
Pour out indulgence still, in measure
As liberal as ye can !

Our Travellers, ye remember well,
Are thridding a sequestered lane ;
And Peter many tricks is trying,
And many anodynes applying,
To ease his conscience of its pain.

By this his heart is lighter far ;
And, finding that he can account
So snugly for that crimson stain,
His evil spirit up again
Does like an empty bucket mount.

And Peter is a deep logician
Who hath no lack of wit mercurial ;
" Blood drops—leaves rustle—yet," quoth he,
" This poor man never, but for me,
Could have had Christian burial.

" And, say the best you can, 'tis plain,
That here has been some wicked dealing ;
No doubt the devil in me wrought ;
I'm not the man who could have thought
An Ass like this was worth the stealing ! "

So from his pocket Peter takes
His shining horn tobacco-box ;
And, in a light and careless way,
As men who with their purpose play,
Upon the lid he knocks.

Let them whose voice can stop the clouds,
Whose cunning eye can see the wind,
Tell to a curious world the cause
Why, making here a sudden pause,
The Ass turned round his head, and *grinned*.

Appalling process ! I have marked
The like on heath, in lonely wood ;
And, verily, have seldom met
A spectacle more hideous—yet
It suited Peter's present mood.

And, grinning in his turn, his teeth
He in jocose defiance showed—
When, to upset his spiteful mirth,
A murmur, pent within the earth,
In the dead earth beneath the road

Rolled audibly ! it swept along,
A muffled noise—a rumbling sound !—
'Twas by a troop of miners made,
Plying with gunpowder their trade,
Some twenty fathoms under ground.

Small cause of dire effect ! for, surely,
If ever mortal, King or Cotter,
Believed that earth was charged to quake
And yawn for his unworthy sake,
'Twas Peter Bell the Potter.

But, as an oak in breathless air
Will stand though to the centre hewn ;

Or as the weakest things, if frost
Have stiffened them, maintain their post ;
So he, beneath the gazing moon !—

The Beast bestriding thus, he reached
A spot where, in a sheltering cove,
A little chapel stands alone,
With greenest ivy overgrown,
And tufted with an ivy grove ;

Dying insensibly away
From human thoughts and purposes,
It seemed—wall, window, roof and tower
To bow to some transforming power,
And blend with the surrounding trees.

As ruinous a place it was,
Thought Peter, in the shire of Fife
That served my turn, when following still
From land to land a reckless will
I married my sixth wife !

The unheeding Ass moves slowly on,
And now is passing by an inn
Brim-full of a carousing crew,
That make, with curses not a few,
An uproar and a drunken din.

I cannot well express the thoughts
Which Peter in those noises found ;—
A stifling power compressed his frame,
While-as a swimming darkness came
Over that dull and dreary sound.

For well did Peter know the sound ;
The language of those drunken joys
To him, a jovial soul, I ween,
But a few hours ago, had been
A gladsome and a welcome noise.

Now, turned adrift into the past,
He finds no solace in his course ;
Like planet-stricken men of yore,
He trembles, smitten to the core
By strong compunction and remorse.

But, more than all, his heart is stung
To think of one, almost a child ;
A sweet and playful Highland girl,
As light and beauteous as a squirrel,
As beauteous and as wild !

Her dwelling was a lonely house,
A cottage in a heathy dell ;
And she put on her gown of green,
And left her mother at sixteen,
And followed Peter Bell.

But many good and pious thoughts
Had she ; and, in the kirk to pray,
Two long Scotch miles, through rain or snow
To kirk she had been used to go,
Twice every Sabbath-day.

And, when she followed Peter Bell,
It was to lead an honest life ;
For he, with tongue not used to falter,
Had pledged his troth before the altar
To love her as his wedded wife.

A mother's hope is hers ;—but soon
She drooped and pined like one forlorn ;—
From Scripture she a name did borrow ;
Benoni, or the child of sorrow,
She called her babe unborn.

For she had learned how Peter lived,
And took it in most grievous part ;

She to the very bone was worn,
And, ere that little child was born,
Died of a broken heart.

And now the Spirits of the Mind
Are busy with poor Peter Bell;
Upon the rights of visual sense
Usurping, with a prevalence
More terrible than magic spell.

Close by a brake of flowering furze
(Above it shivering aspens play)
He sees an unsubstantial creature,
His very self in form and feature,
Not four yards from the broad highway:

And stretched beneath the furze he sees
The Highland girl—it is no other;
And hears her crying as she cried,
The very moment that she died,
" My mother! oh my mother!"

The sweat pours down from Peter's face,
So grievous is his heart's contrition;
With agony his eye-balls ache
While he beholds by the furze-brake
This miserable vision!

Calm is the well-deserving brute,
His peace hath no offence betrayed;
But now, while down that slope he wends
A voice to Peter's ear ascends,
Resounding from the woody glade:

The voice, though clamorous as a horn
Re-echoed by a naked rock,
Comes from that tabernacle—List!
Within, a fervent Methodist
Is preaching to no heedless flock!

" Repent ! repent ! " he cries aloud,
" While yet ye may find mercy ;—strive
To love the Lord with all your might ;
Turn to him, seek him day and night,
And save your souls alive !

" Repent ! repent ! though ye have gone,
Through paths of wickedness and woe,
After the Babylonian harlot ;
And, though your sins be red as scarlet,
They shall be white as snow ! "

Even as he passed the door, these words
Did plainly come to Peter's ears ;
And they such joyful tidings were,
The joy was more than he could bear !—
He melted into tears.

Sweet tears of hope and tenderness !
And fast they fell, a plenteous shower !
His nerves, his sinews seemed to melt ;
Through all his iron frame was felt
A gentle, a relaxing, power !

Each fibre of his frame was weak ;
Weak all the animal within ;
But, in its helplessness, grew mild
And gentle as an infant child,
An infant that has known no sin.

'Tis said, meek Beast ! that, through Heaven's grace,
He not unmoved did notice now
The cross upon thy shoulder scored,
For lasting impress, by the Lord
To whom all human-kind shall bow ;

Memorial of his touch—that day
When Jesus humbly deigned to ride,

Entering the proud Jerusalem,
By an immeasurable stream
Of shouting people deified !

Meanwhile the persevering Ass
Turned towards a gate that hung in view
Across a shady lane ; his chest
Against the yielding gate he pressed
And quietly passed through.

And up the stony lane he goes ;
No ghost more softly ever trod ;
Among the stones and pebbles, he
Sets down his hoofs inaudibly,
As if with felt his hoofs were shod.

Along the lane the trusty Ass
Went twice two hundred yards or more,
And no one could have guessed his aim,—
Till to a lonely house he came,
And stopped beside the door.

Thought Peter, 'tis the poor man's home !
He listens—not a sound is heard
Save from the trickling household rill ;
But, stepping o'er the cottage-sill,
Forthwith a little Girl appeared.

She to the Meeting-house was bound
In hopes some tidings there to gather :
No glimpse it is, no doubtful gleam ;
She saw—and uttered with a scream,
" My father ! here's my father ! "

The very word was plainly heard,
Heard plainly by the wretched Mother
Her joy was like a deep affright :
And forth she rushed into the light
And saw it was another !

And, instantly, upon the earth,
Beneath the full moon shining bright,
Close to the Ass's feet she fell ;
At the same moment Peter Bell
Dismounts in most unhappy plight.

As he beheld the Woman lie
Breathless and motionless, the mind
Of Peter sadly was confused ;
But, though to such demands unused,
And helpless almost as the blind,

He raised her up ; and, while he held
Her body propped against his knee,
The Woman waked—and when she spied
The poor Ass standing by her side,
She moaned most bitterly.

" Oh ! God be praised—my heart's at ease—
For he is dead—I know it well ! "
—At this she wept a bitter flood ;
And, in the best way that he could,
His tale did Peter tell.

He trembles—he is pale as death ;
His voice is weak with perturbation ;
He turns aside his head, he pauses ;
Poor Peter, from a thousand causes,
Is crippled sore in his narration.

At length she learned how he espied
The Ass in that small meadow-ground ;
And that her Husband now lay dead,
Beside that luckless river's bed
In which he had been drowned.

A piercing look the Widow cast
Upon the Beast that near her stands ;

She sees 'tis he, that 'tis the same;
She calls the poor Ass by his name,
And wrings, and wrings her hands.

" O wretched loss—untimely stroke!
If he had died upon his bed!
He knew not one forewarning pain;
He never will come home again—
Is dead, for ever dead!"

Beside the woman Peter stands;
His heart is opening more and more;
A holy sense pervades his mind;
He feels what he for human kind
Had never felt before.

At length, by Peter's arm sustained,
The Woman rises from the ground—
" Oh, mercy! something must be done,
My little Rachel, you must run,—
Some willing neighbour must be found.

" Make haste—my little Rachel—do,
The first you meet with—bid him come,
Ask him to lend his horse to-night,
And this good Man, whom Heaven requite,
Will help to bring the body home."

Away goes Rachel weeping loud;—
An infant, waked by her distress,
Makes in the house a piteous cry;
And Peter hears the Mother sigh,
" Seven are they, and all fatherless!"

And now is Peter taught to feel
That man's heart is a holy thing;
And Nature, through a world of death,
Breathes into him a second breath,
More searching than the breath of spring.

Upon a stone the Woman sits
In agony of silent grief—
From his own thoughts did Peter start ;
He longs to press her to his heart,
From love that cannot find relief.

But roused, as if through every limb
Had past a sudden shock of dread,
The Mother o'er the threshold flies,
And up the cottage stairs she hies,
And on the pillow lays her burning head.

And Peter turns his steps aside
Into a shade of darksome trees,
Where he sits down, he knows not how,
With his hands pressed against his brow,
His elbows on his tremulous knees.

There, self-involved, does Peter sit
Until no sign of life he makes,
As if his mind were sinking deep
Through years that have been long asleep.
The trance is passed away—he wakes ;

He lifts his head—and sees the Ass
Yet standing in the clear moonshine ;
" When shall I be as good as thou ?
Oh ! would, poor beast, that I had now
A heart but half as good as thine ! "

But *He*—who deviously hath sought
His Father through the lonesome woods,
Hath sought, proclaiming to the ear
Of night his grief and sorrowful fear—
He comes, escaped from fields and floods ;—

With weary pace is drawing nigh ;
He sees the Ass—and nothing living

Had ever such a fit of joy
As hath this little orphan Boy,
For he has no misgiving !

Forth to the gentle Ass he springs,
And up about his neck he climbs ;
In loving words he talks to him,
He kisses, kisses face and limb,—
He kisses him a thousand times !

This Peter sees, while in the shade
He stood beside the cottage-door ;
And Peter Bell, the ruffian wild,
Sobs loud, he sobs even like a child,
" O God ! I can endure no more ! "

—Here ends my Tale : for in a trice
Arrived a neighbour with his horse ;
Peter went forth with him straightway ;
And, with due care, ere break of day,
Together they brought back the Corse.

And many years did this poor Ass,
Whom once it was my luck to see
Cropping the shrubs of Leming-Lane,
Help by his labour to maintain
The Widow and her family

And Peter Bell, who, till that night,
Had been the wildest of his clan,
Forsook his crimes, renounced his folly,
And, after ten months' melancholy,
Became a good and honest man.

A POEM OF RETRIBUTION BY COLERIDGE

The Rime of the Ancient Mariner

In Seven Parts

1798

Facile credo, plures esse Naturas invisibiles quam visibiles in rerum universitate. Sed horum omnium familiam quis nobis enarrabit, et gradus et cognationes et discrimina et singulorum munera ? Quid agunt ? quæ loca habitant ? Harum rerum notitiam semper ambivit ingenium humanum, nunquam attigit. Juvat, interea, non diffiteor, quandoque in animo, tanquam in tabulâ, majoris et melioris mundi imaginem contemplari : ne mens assuefacta hodiernæ vitæ minutiis se contrahat nimis, et tota subsidat in pusillas cogitationes. Sed veritati interea invigilandum est, modusque servandus, ut certa ab incertis, diem a nocte, distinguamus. — T. BURNET : *Archæol. Phil.*, p. 68.

PART THE FIRST

An ancient
Mariner meet-
eth three gal-
lants bidden
to a wedding-
feast, and de-
taineth one.

IT is an ancient Mariner,
And he stoppeth one of three.
" By thy long grey beard and glittering eye,
Now wherefore stopp'st thou me ?

The Bridegroom's doors are opened wide,
And I am next of kin ;
The guests are met, the feast is set :
May'st hear the merry din."

He holds him with his skinny hand,
" There was a ship," quoth he,
" Hold off ! unhand me, grey beard loon ! "
Eftsoons his hand dropt he.

He holds him with his glittering eye—
The Wedding-Guest stood still,
And listens like a three years' child ;
The Mariner hath his will.

The Wedding-Guest is spellbound by the eye of the old sea-faring man, and constrained to hear his tale.

The Wedding-Guest sat on a stone ;
He cannot choose but hear ;
And thus spake on that ancient man,
The bright-eyed Mariner.

" The ship was cheered, the harbour cleared,
Merrily did we drop
Below the kirk, below the hill,
Below the lighthouse top.

The Sun came up upon the left,
Out of the sea came he !
And he shone bright, and on the right
Went down into the sea.

The Mariner tells how the ship sailed southward with a good wind and fair weather, till it reached the Line.

Higher and higher every day,
Till over the mast at noon—"
The Wedding-Guest here beat his breast,
For he heard the loud bassoon.

The bride hath paced into the hall,
Red as a rose is she ;
Nodding their heads before her goes
The merry minstrelsy.

The Wedding-Guest heareth the bridal music ; but the Mariner continueth his tale.

The Wedding-Guest he beat his breast,
Yet he cannot choose but hear ;
And thus spake on that ancient man,
The bright-eyed Mariner.

The ship
driven by a
storm toward
the south pole.
" And now the storm-blast came, and he
Was tyrannous and strong :
He struck with his o'ertaking wings,
And chased us south along.

With sloping masts and dipping prow,
As who pursued with yell and blow
Still treads the shadow of his foe
And forward bends his head,
The ship drove fast, loud roared the blast,
And southward aye we fled.

And now there came both mist and snow,
And it grew wondrous cold :
And ice, mast-high, came floating by,
As green as emerald.

The land of
ice, and of
fearful sounds,
where no
living thing
was to be seen.
And through the drifts the snowy clifts
Did send a dismal sheen :
Nor shapes of men nor beasts we ken—
The ice was all between.

The ice was here, the ice was there,
The ice was all around :
It cracked and growled, and roared and
          howled,
Like noises in a swound !

Till a great
sea-bird,
called the
Albatross,
came through
the snow-fog,
and was re-
ceived with
great joy and
hospitality.
At length did cross an Albatross :
Through the fog it came ;
As if it had been a Christian soul,
We hailed it in God's name.

It ate the food it ne'er had eat,
And round and round it flew.
The ice did split with a thunder-fit ;
The helmsman steered us through !

And a good south wind sprung up behind ;
The Albatross did follow,
And every day, for food or play,
Came to the mariners' hollo !

In mist or cloud, on mast or shroud,
It perched for vespers nine ;
Whiles all the night, through fog-smoke
    white,
Glimmered the white Moon-shine."

"God save thee, ancient Mariner !
From the fiends, that plague thee thus !—
Why look'st thou so ?"—"With my cross-
    bow
I shot the Albatross.

PART THE SECOND

The Sun now rose upon the right :
Out of the sea came he,
Still hid in mist, and on the left
Went down into the sea.

And the good south wind still blew behind,
But no sweet bird did follow,
Nor any day, for food or play,
Came to the mariners' hollo !

And I had done a hellish thing,
And it would work 'em woe :
For all averred, I had killed the bird
That made the breeze to blow.
Ah, wretch ! said they, the bird to slay,
That made the breeze to blow !

And lo ! the Albatross proveth a bird of good omen, and followeth the ship as it returned northward through fog and floating ice.

The ancient Mariner inhospitably killeth the pious bird of good omen.

His shipmates cry out against the ancient Mariner, for killing the bird of good luck.

But when the fog cleared off, they justify the same, and thus make themselves accomplices in the crime.

Nor dim nor red, like God's own head,
The glorious Sun uprist ;
Then all averred, I had killed the bird
That brought the fog and mist.
'Twas right, said they, such birds to slay,
That bring the fog and mist.

The fair breeze continues ; the ship enters the Pacific Ocean and sails northward, even till it reaches the Line.

The ship hath been suddenly becalmed.

The fair breeze blew, the white foam flew,
The furrow followed free :
We were the first that ever burst
Into that silent sea.

Down dropt the breeze, the sails dropt
    down,
'Twas sad as sad could be ;
And we did speak only to break
The silence of the sea !

All in a hot and copper sky,
The bloody Sun, at noon,
Right up above the mast did stand,
No bigger than the Moon.

Day after day, day after day,
We stuck, nor breath nor motion ;
As idle as a painted ship
Upon a painted ocean.

And the Albatross begins to be avenged.

Water, water, every where,
And all the boards did shrink ;
Water, water, every where,
Nor any drop to drink.

The very deep did rot : O Christ !
That ever this should be !
Yea, slimy things did crawl with legs
Upon the slimy sea.

About, about, in reel and rout
The death-fires danced at night ;
The water, like a witch's oils,
Burnt green, and blue, and white.

And some in dreams assured were
Of the spirit that plagued us so :
Nine fathom deep he had followed us
From the land of mist and snow.

A Spirit had
followed
them ; one of
the invisible
inhabitants
of this planet,
neither departed souls nor angels ; concerning whom the learned
Jew, Josephus, and the Platonic Constantinopolitan, Michael
Psellus, may be consulted. They are very numerous, and there is
no climate or element without one or more.

And every tongue, through utter drought,
Was withered at the root ;
We could not speak, no more than if
We had been choked with soot.

Ah ! well-a-day ! what evil looks
Had I from old and young !
Instead of the cross, the Albatross
About my neck was hung.

The ship-
mates in their
sore distress
would fain
throw the
whole guilt on
the dead sea-bird
the ancient Mariner : in sign whereof they hang the
round his neck.

PART THE THIRD

THERE passed a weary time. Each throat
Was parched, and glazed each eye.
A weary time ! a weary time !
How glazed each weary eye,
When looking westward I beheld
A something in the sky.

The ancient
Mariner
beholdeth a
sign in the
element afar
off.

At first it seemed a little speck,
And then it seemed a mist :
It moved and moved, and took at last
A certain shape, I wist.

A speck, a mist, a shape, I wist !
And still it neared and neared :
As if it dodged a water-sprite,
It plunged and tacked and veered.

At its nearer approach, it seemeth him to be a ship ; and at a dear ransom he freeth his speech from the bonds of thirst.

With throats unslaked, with black lips baked,
We could nor laugh nor wail ;
Through utter drought all dumb we stood !
I bit my arm, I sucked the blood,
And cried, A sail ! a sail !

With throats unslaked, with black lips baked,
Agape they heard me call :
A flash of joy.
Gramercy ! they for joy did grin,
And all at once their breath drew in,
As they were drinking all.

And horror follows. For can it be a *ship* that comes onward without wind or tide ?

See ! see ! (I cried) she tacks no more !
Hither to work us weal ;
Without a breeze, without a tide,
She steadies with upright keel !

The western wave was all a-flame,
The day was well-nigh done !
Almost upon the western wave
Rested the broad bright Sun ;
When that strange shape drove suddenly
Betwixt us and the Sun.

It seemeth him but the skeleton of a ship.

And straight the Sun was flecked with bars
(Heaven's Mother send us grace !)
As if through a dungeon-grate he peered,
With broad and burning face.

Alas ! (thought I, and my heart beat loud,)
How fast she nears and nears !
Are those her sails that glance in the Sun,
Like restless gossameres ?

Are those her ribs through which the Sun
Did peer, as through a grate ?
And is that Woman all her crew ?
Is that a Death ? and are there two ?
Is Death that woman's mate ?

And its ribs are seen as bars on the face of the setting Sun.

The spectre-woman and her death-mate, and no other on board the skeleton-ship.

Her lips were red, her looks were free,
Her locks were yellow as gold :
Her skin was as white as leprosy,
The Night-mare Life-in-Death was she,
Who thicks man's blood with cold.

Like vessel, like crew !

The naked hulk alongside came,
And the twain were casting dice ;
' The game is done ! I've won, I've won ! '
Quoth she, and whistles thrice.

Death and Life-in-Death have diced for the ship's crew, and she (the latter) winneth the ancient Mariner.

The Sun's rim dips ; the stars rush out :
At one stride comes the dark :
With far-heard whisper o'er the sea,
Off shot the spectre-bark.

No twilight within the courts of the Sun.

We listened and looked sideways up !
Fear at my heart, as at a cup,
My life-blood seemed to sip !
The stars were dim, and thick the night,
The steersman's face by his lamp gleamed white ;
From the sails the dew did drip—
Till clomb above the eastern bar
The horned Moon, with one bright star
Within the nether tip.

At the rising of the Moon.

One after another,	One after one, by the star-dogged Moon, Too quick for groan or sigh, Each turned his face with a ghastly pang, And cursed me with his eye.
His shipmates drop down dead.	Four times fifty living men (And I heard nor sigh nor groan), With heavy thump, a lifeless lump, They dropped down one by one.
But Life-in-Death begins her work on the ancient Mariner.	The souls did from their bodies fly,— They fled to bliss or woe! And every soul, it passed me by, Like the whizz of my cross-bow!"

PART THE FOURTH

The Wedding-Guest feareth that a spirit is talking to him;	"I FEAR thee, ancient Mariner! I fear thy skinny hand! And thou art long, and lank, and brown, As is the ribbed sea-sand.*
	I fear thee, and thy glittering eye, And thy skinny hand, so brown."——
But the ancient Mariner assureth him of his bodily life, and proceedeth to relate his horrible penance.	"Fear not, fear not, thou Wedding-Guest! This body dropt not down. Alone, alone, all, all alone, Alone on a wide wide sea! And never a saint took pity on My soul in agony.
He despiseth the creatures of the calm.	The many men, so beautiful! And they all dead did lie; And a thousand thousand slimy things Lived on; and so did I.

* For the last two lines of this stanza, I am indebted to Mr. Words-worth. It was on a delightful walk from Nether Stowey to Dulverton, with him and his sister, in the Autumn of 1797, that this Poem was planned, and in part composed.

I looked upon the rotting sea,
And drew my eyes away ;
I looked upon the rotting deck,
And there the dead men lay.

I looked to Heaven, and tried to pray ;
But or ever a prayer had gusht,
A wicked whisper came, and made
My heart as dry as dust.

I closed my lids, and kept them close,
And the balls like pulses beat ;
For the sky and the sea, and the sea and
    the sky,
Lay like a load on my weary eye,
And the dead were at my feet.

The cold sweat melted from their limbs,
Nor rot nor reek did they :
The look with which they looked on me
Had never passed away.

An orphan's curse would drag to hell
A spirit from on high ;
But oh ! more horrible than that
Is the curse in a dead man's eye !
Seven days, seven nights, I saw that curse,
And yet I could not die.

The moving Moon went up the sky
And no where did abide :
Softly she was going up,
And a star or two beside—

Moon, and the stars that still sojourn, yet still move onward ; and
everywhere the blue sky belongs to them, and is their appointed
rest, and their native country and their own natural homes, which
they enter unannounced, as lords that are certainly expected and yet
there is a silent joy at their arrival.

Her beams bemocked the sultry main,
Like April hoar-frost spread ;
But where the ship's huge shadow lay,
The charmed water burnt alway
A still and awful red.

By the light
of the Moon
he beholdeth
God's
creatures of
the great
calm.

Beyond the shadow of the ship,
I watched the water-snakes :
They moved in tracks of shining white,
And when they reared, the elfish light
Fell off in hoary flakes.

Within the shadow of the ship
I watched their rich attire :
Blue, glossy green, and velvet black,
They coiled and swam ; and every track
Was a flash of golden fire.

Their beauty
and their
happiness.

He blesseth
them in his
heart.

O happy living things ! no tongue
Their beauty might declare :
A spring of love gushed from my heart,
And I blessed them unaware :
Sure my kind saint took pity on me,
And I blessed them unaware.

The spell
begins to
break.

The self-same moment I could pray ;
And from my neck so free
The Albatross fell off, and sank
Like lead into the sea.

PART THE FIFTH

Oh sleep ! it is a gentle thing,
Beloved from pole to pole !
To Mary Queen the praise be given !
She sent the gentle sleep from Heaven,
That slid into my soul.

The silly buckets on the deck,
That had so long remained,
I dreamt that they were filled with dew ;
And when I awoke, it rained.

By grace of
the holy
Mother, the
ancient
Mariner is re-
freshed with
rain.

My lips were wet, my throat was cold,
My garments were all dank ;
Sure I had drunken in my dreams,
And still my body drank.

I moved, and could not feel my limbs :
I was so light—almost
I thought that I had died in sleep,
And was a blessed ghost.

And soon I heard a roaring wind :
It did not come anear ;
But with its sound it shook the sails,
That were so thin and sere.

He heareth
sounds, and
seeth strange
sights and
commotions
in the sky and
the element.

The upper air burst into life !
And a hundred fire-flags sheen,
To and fro they were hurried about !
And to and fro, and in and out,
The wan stars danced between.

And the coming wind did roar more loud,
And the sails did sigh like sedge ;
And the rain poured down from one black
        cloud ;
The Moon was at its edge.

The thick black cloud was cleft, and still
The Moon was at its side :
Like waters shot from some high crag,
The lightning fell with never a jag,
A river steep and wide.

The bodies of
the ship's crew
are inspired,
and the ship
moves on;

The loud wind never reached the ship,
Yet now the ship moved on !
Beneath the lightning and the Moon
The dead men gave a groan.

They groaned, they stirred, they all up-
        rose,
Nor spake, nor moved their eyes :
It had been strange, even in a dream,
To have seen those dead men rise.

The helmsman steered, the ship moved on ;
Yet never a breeze up blew ;
The mariners all 'gan work the ropes,
Where they were wont to do :
They raised their limbs like lifeless tools—
We were a ghastly crew.

The body of my brother's son
Stood by me, knee to knee :
The body and I pulled at one rope,
But he said nought to me."

But not by
the souls of
the men, nor
by dæmons
of earth or
middle air,
but by a
blessed troop
of angelic
spirits, sent
down by the
invocation of
the guardian
saint.

" I fear thee, ancient Mariner ! "
" Be calm, thou Wedding-Guest !
'Twas not those souls that fled in pain,
Which to their corses came again,
But a troop of spirits blest :

For when it dawned—they dropped their
        arms,
And clustered round the mast ;
Sweet sounds rose slowly through their
        mouths,
And from their bodies passed.

Around, around, flew each sweet sound,
Then darted to the Sun ;
Slowly the sounds came back again,
Now mixed, now one by one.

Sometimes a-dropping from the sky
I heard the sky-lark sing ;
Sometimes all little birds that are,
How they seemed to fill the sea and air
With their sweet jargoning !

And now 'twas like all instruments,
Now like a lonely flute ;
And now it is an angel's song,
That makes the Heavens be mute.

It ceased ; yet still the sails made on
A pleasant noise till noon,
A noise like of a hidden brook
In the leafy month of June,
That to the sleeping woods all night
Singeth a quiet tune.

Till noon we quietly sailed on,
Yet never a breeze did breathe :
Slowly and smoothly went the ship,
Moved onward from beneath.

Under the keel nine fathom deep,
From the land of mist and snow,
The spirit slid : and it was he
That made the ship to go.
The sails at noon left off their tune,
And the ship stood still also.

The Sun, right up above the mast,
Had fixed her to the ocean :

The lonesome Spirit from the south pole carries on the ship as far as the Line, in obedience to the angelic troop, but still requireth vengeance.

But in a minute she 'gan stir,
With a short uneasy motion—
Backwards and forwards half her length
With a short uneasy motion.

Then like a pawing horse let go,
She made a sudden bound :
It flung the blood into my head,
And I fell down in a swound.

How long in that same fit I lay,
I have not to declare ;
But ere my living life returned,
I heard and in my soul discerned
Two voices in the air.

' Is it he ? ' quoth one, ' Is this the man ?
By him who died on cross,
With his cruel bow he laid full low
The harmless Albatross.

The spirit who bideth by himself
In the land of mist and snow,
He loved the bird that loved the man
Who shot him with his bow.'

The other was a softer voice,
As soft as honey-dew :
Quoth he, ' The man hath penance done,
And penance more will do.'

The Polar Spirit's fellow-dæmons, the invisible inhabitants of the element, take part in his wrong ; and two of them relate, one to the other, that penance long and heavy for the ancient Mariner hath been accorded to the Polar Spirit, who returneth southward.

PART THE SIXTH

First Voice

' BUT tell me, tell me ! speak again,
Thy soft response renewing—
What makes that ship drive on so fast
What is the ocean doing ? '

Second Voice

' Still as a slave before his lord,
The ocean hath no blast ;
His great bright eye most silently
Up to the Moon is cast—

If he may know which way to go ;
For she guides him smooth or grim.
See, brother, see ! how graciously
She looketh down on him.'

First Voice

' But why drives on that ship so fast,
Without a wave or wind ? '

Second Voice

' The air is cut away before,
And closes from behind.

Fly, brother, fly ! more high, more high !
Or we shall be belated :
For slow and slow that ship will go,
When the Mariner's trance is abated.'

I woke, and we were sailing on
As in a gentle weather :
'Twas night, calm night, the Moon was high ;
The dead men stood together.

All stood together on the deck,
For a charnel-dungeon fitter :
All fixed on me their stony eyes,
That in the Moon did glitter.

The pang, the curse, with which they died,
Had never passed away :
I could not draw my eyes from theirs,
Nor turn them up to pray.

The Mariner hath been cast into a trance ; for the angelic power causeth the vessel to drive northward faster than human life could endure.

The supernatural motion is retarded ; the Mariner awakes, and his penance begins anew.

The curse
is finally
expiated.

And now this spell was snapt : once more
I viewed the ocean green,
And looked far forth, yet little saw
Of what had else been seen—

Like one, that on a lonesome road
Doth walk in fear and dread,
And having once turned round walks on
And turns no more his head ;
Because he knows, a frightful fiend
Doth close behind him tread.

But soon there breathed a wind on me,
Nor sound nor motion made :
Its path was not upon the sea,
In ripple or in shade.

It raised my hair, it fanned my cheek
Like a meadow-gale of spring—
It mingled strangely with my fears,
Yet it felt like a welcoming.

Swiftly, swiftly flew the ship,
Yet she sailed softly too :
Sweetly, sweetly blew the breeze—
On me alone it blew.

And the
ancient Mari-
ner beholdeth
his native
country.

Oh ! dream of joy ! is this indeed
The light-house top I see ?
Is this the hill ? is this the kirk ?
Is this mine own countree ?

We drifted o'er the harbour-bar,
And I with sobs did pray—
O let me be awake, my God !
Or let me sleep alway.

The harbour-bay was clear as glass,
So smoothly it was strewn !
And on the bay the moonlight lay,
And the shadow of the Moon.

The rock shone bright, the kirk no less,
That stands above the rock :
The moonlight steeped in silentness
The steady weathercock.

And the bay was white with silent light,
Till rising from the same,
Full many shapes, that shadows were,
In crimson colours came.

The angelic spirits leave the dead bodies,

A little distance from the prow
Those crimson shadows were :
I turned my eyes upon the deck—
Oh, Christ ! what saw I there !

And appear in their own forms of light.

Each corse lay flat, lifeless and flat,
And, by the holy rood !
A man all light, a seraph man,
On every corse there stood.

This seraph-band, each waved his hand :
It was a heavenly sight !
They stood as signals to the land,
Each one a lovely light ;

This seraph-band, each waved his hand,
No voice did they impart—
No voice ; but oh ! the silence sank
Like music on my heart.

But soon I heard the dash of oars,
I heard the Pilot's cheer ;
My head was turned perforce away,
And I saw a boat appear.

The Pilot, and the Pilot's boy,
I heard them coming fast :
Dear Lord in Heaven ! it was a joy
The dead men could not blast.

I saw a third—I heard his voice :
It is the Hermit good !
He singeth loud his godly hymns
That he makes in the wood.
He'll shrieve my soul, he'll wash away
The Albatross's blood.

PART THE SEVENTH

The Hermit
of the Wood,

THIS Hermit good lives in that wood
Which slopes down to the sea.
How loudly his sweet voice he rears !
He loves to talk with marineres
That come from a far countree.

He kneels at morn, and noon, and eve—
He hath a cushion plump :
It is the moss that wholly hides
The rotted old oak-stump.

The skiff-boat neared : I heard them talk,
' Why, this is strange, I trow !
Where are those lights so many and fair,
That signal made but now ? '

Approacheth
the ship with
wonder.

' Strange, by my faith ! ' the Hermit said—
' And they answered not our cheer !
The planks looked warped ! and see those
     sails,
How thin they are and sere !
I never saw aught like to them.
Unless perchance it were

Brown skeletons of leaves that lag
My forest-brook along ;
When the ivy-tod is heavy with snow,
And the owlet whoops to the wolf below,
That eats the she-wolf's young.'

' Dear Lord ! it hath a fiendish look—
(The Pilot made reply)
I am a-feared '—' Push on, push on ! '
Said the Hermit cheerily.

The boat came closer to the ship,
But I nor spake nor stirred ;
The boat came close beneath the ship,
And straight a sound was heard.

Under the water it rumbled on,
Still louder and more dread :
It reached the ship, it split the bay ;
The ship went down like lead.

The ship suddenly sinketh.

Stunned by that loud and dreadful sound,
Which sky and ocean smote,
Like one that hath been seven days drowned
My body lay afloat ;
But swift as dreams, myself I found
Within the Pilot's boat.

The ancient Mariner is saved in the Pilot's boat.

Upon the whirl, where sank the ship,
The boat spun round and round ;
And all was still, save that the hill
Was telling of the sound.

I moved my lips—the Pilot shrieked
And fell down in a fit ;
The holy Hermit raised his eyes,
And prayed where he did sit.

I took the oars : the Pilot's boy,
Who now doth crazy go,
Laughed loud and long, and all the while
His eyes went to and fro.
' Ha ! ha ! ' quoth he, ' full plain I see,
The Devil knows how to row.'

And now, all in my own countree,
I stood on the firm land !
The Hermit stepped forth from the boat,
And scarcely he could stand.

' O shrieve me, shrieve me, holy man ! '
The Hermit crossed his brow.
' Say quick,' quoth he, ' I bid thee say—
What manner of man art thou ? '

Forthwith this frame of mine was wrenched
With a woeful agony,
Which forced me to begin my tale ;
And then it left me free.

Since then, at an uncertain hour,
That agony returns ;
And till my ghastly tale is told,
This heart within me burns.

I pass, like night, from land to land ;
I have strange power of speech ;
That moment that his face I see,
I know the man that must hear me :
To him my tale I teach.

What loud uproar bursts from that door !
The wedding-guests are there :
But in the garden-bower the bride
And bride-maids singing are :
And hark the little vesper bell,
Which biddeth me to prayer !

O Wedding-Guest ! this soul hath been
Alone on a wide wide sea :
So lonely 'twas that God himself
Scarce seemed there to be.

O sweeter than the marriage feast,
'Tis sweeter far to me,
To walk together to the kirk
With a goodly company !—

To walk together to the kirk,
And all together pray,
While each to his great Father bends
Old men, and babes, and loving friends,
And youths and maidens gay !

Farewell, farewell ! but this I tell   And to teach,
To thee, thou Wedding-Guest !   by his own
He prayeth well, who loveth well   example. love
                                            and reverence
Both man and bird and beast.   to all things
                                            that God
                                            made and
He prayeth best, who loveth best   loveth.
All things both great and small ;
For the dear God who loveth us,
He made and loveth all."

The Mariner, whose eye is bright,
Whose beard with age is hoar,
Is gone : and now the Wedding-Guest
Turned from the bridegroom's door.

He went like one that hath been stunned,
And is of sense forlorn :
A sadder and a wiser man,
He rose the morrow morn.

NATIONAL POEMS BY WORDSWORTH

On the Extinction of the Venetian Republic

ONCE did She hold the gorgeous east in fee ;
And was the safeguard of the west : the worth
Of Venice did not fall below her birth,
Venice, the eldest Child of Liberty.
She was a maiden City, bright and free ;
No guile seduced, no force could violate ;
And, when she took unto herself a Mate,
She must espouse the everlasting Sea.
And what if she had seen those glories fade,
Those titles vanish, and that strength decay ;
Yet shall some tribute of regret be paid
When her long life hath reached its final day :
Men are we, and must grieve when even the Shade
Of that which once was great is passed away.

To Toussaint L'Ouverture

TOUSSAINT, the most unhappy man of men !
Whether the whistling Rustic tend his plough
Within thy hearing, or thy head be now
Pillowed in some deep dungeon's earless den ;—
O miserable Chieftain ! where and when
Wilt thou find patience ?   Yet die not ; do thou
Wear rather in thy bonds a cheerful brow :
Though fallen thyself, never to rise again,
Live, and take comfort.   Thou hast left behind
Powers that will work for thee ; air, earth, and skies ;

There's not a breathing of the common wind
That will forget thee ; thou hast great allies ;
Thy friends are exultations, agonies,
And love, and man's unconquerable mind.

Written in London, September 1802

O FRIEND ! I know not which way I must look
For comfort, being, as I am, opprest,
To think that now our life is only drest
For show ; mean handy-work of craftsman, cook,
Or groom !—We must run glittering like a brook
In the open sunshine, or we are unblest :
The wealthiest man among us is the best :
No grandeur now in nature or in book
Delights us.   Rapine, avarice, expense,
This is idolatry ; and these we adore :
Plain living and high thinking are no more :
The homely beauty of the good old cause
Is gone ; our peace, our fearful innocence,
And pure religion breathing household laws.

London, 1802

MILTON ! thou should'st be living at this hour :
England hath need of thee : she is a fen
Of stagnant waters : altar, sword, and pen,
Fireside, the heroic wealth of hall and bower,
Have forfeited their ancient English dower
Of inward happiness.   We are selfish men ;
Oh ! raise us up, return to us again ;
And give us manners, virtue, freedom, power.
Thy soul was like a Star, and dwelt apart :
Thou hadst a voice whose sound was like the sea :
Pure as the naked heavens, majestic, free,
So didst thou travel on life's common way,
In cheerful godliness ; and yet thy heart
The lowliest duties on herself did lay.

" Great Men have been among Us "

GREAT men have been among us ; hands that penned
And tongues that uttered wisdom—better none :
The later Sidney, Marvel, Harrington,
Young Vane, and others who called Milton friend.
These moralists could act and comprehend :
They knew how genuine glory was put on ;
Taught us how rightfully a nation shone
In splendour : what strength was, that would not bend
But in magnanimous meekness.   France, 'tis strange,
Hath brought forth no such souls as we had then.
Perpetual emptiness ! unceasing change !
No single volume paramount, no code,
No master spirit, no determined road ;
But equally a want of books and men !

" It is not to be thought of "

IT is not to be thought of that the Flood
Of British freedom, which, to the open sea
Of the world's praise, from dark antiquity
Hath flowed, " with pomp of waters, unwithstood,"
Roused though it be full often to a mood
Which spurns the check of salutary bands,
That this most famous Stream in bogs and sands
Should perish ; and to evil and to good
Be lost for ever.   In our halls is hung
Armoury of the invincible Knights of old :
We must be free or die, who speak the tongue
That Shakespeare spake ; the faith and morals hold
Which Milton held.—In everything we are sprung
Of Earth's first blood, have titles manifold.

To the Men of Kent

October 1803

VANGUARD of Liberty, ye men of Kent,
Ye children of a Soil that doth advance
Her haughty brow against the coast of France,
Now is the time to prove your hardiment !
To France be words of invitation sent !
They from their fields can see the countenance
Of your fierce war, may ken the glittering lance,
And hear you shouting forth your brave intent.
Left single, in bold parley, ye, of yore,
Did from the Norman win a gallant wreath ;
Confirmed the charters that were yours before ;—
No parleying now !   In Britain is one breath ;
We all are with you now from shore to shore :—
Ye men of Kent, 'tis victory or death !

November 1806

ANOTHER year !—another deadly blow !
Another mighty Empire overthrown !
And We are left, or shall be left, alone ;
The last that dare to struggle with the Foe.
'Tis well ! from this day forward we shall know
That in ourselves our safety must be sought ;
That by our own right hands it must be wrought;
That we must stand unpropped, or be laid low.
O dastard whom such foretaste doth not cheer !
We shall exult, if they who rule the land
Be men who hold its many blessings dear,
Wise, upright, valiant ; not a servile band,
Who are to judge of danger which they fear,
And honour which they do not understand.

NATIONAL POEMS BY COLERIDGE

Ode to the Departing Year *

ARGUMENT

[The Ode commences with an address to the Divine Providence,
that regulates into one vast harmony all the events of time, however
calamitous some of them may appear to mortals.   The second
Strophe calls on men to suspend their private joys and sorrows, and
devote them for a while to the cause of human nature in general.
The first Epode speaks of the Empress of Russia, who died of an
apoplexy on the 17th of November 1796 ; having just concluded a
subsidiary treaty with the Kings combined against France.   The
first and second Antistrophe describe the Image of the Departing
Year, etc., as in a vision.   The second Epode prophesies, in anguish
of spirit, the downfall of this country.]

I

SPIRIT who sweepest the wild harp of Time !
   It is most hard, with an untroubled ear
   Thy dark inwoven harmonies to hear !
Yet, mine eye fixed on Heaven's unchanging clime,
Long had I listened, free from mortal fear,
   With inward stillness, and a bowed mind ;
   When lo ! its folds far waving on the wind,
I saw the train of the Departing Year !
      Starting from my silent sadness
      Then with no unholy madness
Ere yet the entered cloud foreclosed my sight,
I raised the impetuous song, and solemnized his flight.

* This Ode was composed on the 24th, 25th, and 26th days of
December 1796 ; and was first published on the last day of that year.

II

Hither, from the recent tomb,
From the prison's direr gloom,
From distemper's midnight anguish ;
And thence, where poverty doth waste and languish !
Or where, his two bright torches blending,
Love illumines manhood's maze ;
Or where o'er cradled infants bending
Hope has fixed her wishful gaze ;
Hither, in perplexed dance,
Ye Woes ! ye young-eyed Joys ! advance !
By Time's wild harp, and by the hand
Whose indefatigable sweep
Raises its fateful strings from sleep,
I bid you haste, a mixed tumultuous band !
From every private bower,
And each domestic hearth,
Haste for one solemn hour ;
And with a loud and yet a louder voice,
O'er Nature struggling in portentous birth,
Weep and rejoice !
Still echoes the dread name that o'er the earth
Let slip the storm, and woke the brood of Hell :
And now advance in saintly jubilee
Justice and Truth !   They too have heard thy spell,
They too obey thy name, divinest Liberty !

III

I marked Ambition in his war-array !
I heard the mailed Monarch's troublous cry—
" Ah ! wherefore does the Northern Conqueress stay !
Groans not her chariot on its onward way ? "
Fly, mailed Monarch, fly !

Stunned by Death's twice mortal mace,
No more on murder's lurid face
The insatiate hag shall gloat with drunken eye !
Manes of the unnumbered slain !
Ye that gasped on Warsaw's plain !
Ye that erst at Ismail's tower,
When human ruin choked the streams,
Fell in conquest's glutted hour,
Mid women's shrieks and infants' screams !
Spirits of the uncoffined slain,
Sudden blasts of triumph swelling,
Oft, at night, in misty train,
Rush around her narrow dwelling !
The exterminating fiend is fled—
(Foul her life, and dark her doom)
Mighty armies of the dead
Dance, like death-fires, round her tomb !
Then with prophetic song relate,
Each some tyrant-murderer's fate !

IV

Departing Year ! 'twas on no earthly shore
My soul beheld thy vision !   Where alone,
Voiceless and stern, before the cloudy throne,
Aye Memory sits : thy robe inscribed with gore,
With many an unimaginable groan
Thou storied'st thy sad hours !   Silence ensued,
Deep silence o'er the ethereal multitude,
Whose locks with wreaths, whose wreaths with glories
shone.
Then, his eye wild ardours glancing,
From the choired gods advancing,
The Spirit of the Earth made reverence meet,
And stood up, beautiful, before the cloudy seat.

V

Throughout the blissful throng,
  Hushed were harp and song :
Till wheeling round the throne the Lampads seven
  (The mystic Words of Heaven),
  Permissive signal make :
The fervent Spirit bowed, then spread his wings and
      spake !
  " Thou in stormy blackness throning
  Love and uncreated Light,
By the Earth's unsolaced groaning,
  Seize thy terrors, Arm of might !
By peace with proffered insult scared,
    Masked hate and envying scorn !
    By years of havoc yet unborn !
And hunger's bosom to the frost-winds bared !
    But chief by Afric's wrongs,
      Strange, horrible, and foul !
    By what deep guilt belongs
To the deaf Synod, ' full of gifts and lies ! '
By wealth's insensate laugh ! by torture's howl !
      Avenger, rise !
  For ever shall the thankless Island scowl,
  Her quiver full, and with unbroken bow ?
Speak ! from thy storm-black Heaven, O speak aloud !
      And on the darkling foe
Open thine eye of fire from some uncertain cloud !
  O dart the flash ! O rise and deal the blow !
The Past to thee, to thee the Future cries !
  Hark ! how wide Nature joins her groans below !
  Rise, God of Nature ! rise."

VI

The voice had ceased, the vision fled ;
Yet still I gasped and reeled with dread.

And ever, when the dream of night
Renews the phantom to my sight,
Cold sweat-drops gather on my limbs ;
  My ears throb hot ; my eye-balls start ;
My brain with horrid tumult swims ;
  Wild is the tempest of my heart ;
And my thick and struggling breath
Imitates the toil of death !
No stranger agony confounds
  The soldier on the war-field spread,
When all foredone with toil and wounds,
  Death-like he dozes among heaps of dead !
(The strife is o'er, the day-light fled,
  And the night-wind clamours hoarse !
See ! the starting wretch's head
  Lies pillowed on a brother's corse !)

VII

Not yet enslaved, not wholly vile,
O Albion !   O my mother Isle !
Thy valleys, fair as Eden's bowers,
Glitter green with sunny showers ;
Thy grassy uplands' gentle swells
  Echo to the bleat of flocks
(Those grassy hills, those glittering dells
  Proudly ramparted with rocks) ;
And Ocean mid his uproar wild
Speaks safety to his island-child.
Hence for many a fearless age
  Has social Quiet loved thy shore ;
Nor ever proud invader's rage
Or sacked thy towers, or stained thy fields with gore

VIII

Abandoned of Heaven ! mad avarice thy guide,
At cowardly distance, yet kindling with pride—

Mid thy herds and thy corn-fields secure thou hast
    stood,
And joined the wild yelling of famine and blood !
The nations curse thee ! They with eager wondering
    Shall hear Destruction, like a vulture, scream !
    Strange-eyed Destruction ! who with many a dream
Of central fires through nether seas upthundering
    Soothes her fierce solitude ; yet as she lies
By livid fount, or red volcanic stream,
    If ever to her lidless dragon-eyes,
    O Albion ! thy predestined ruins rise,
The fiend-hag on her perilous couch doth leap,
Muttering distempered triumph in her charmed sleep.

IX

    Away, my soul, away !
  In vain, in vain the birds of warning sing—
And hark ! I hear the famished brood of prey
Flap their lank pennons on the groaning wind !
    Away, my soul, away !
I, unpartaking of the evil thing,
    With daily prayer and daily toil
    Soliciting for food my scanty soil,
Have wailed my country with a loud Lament.
Now I recentre my immortal mind
    In the deep sabbath of meek self-content ;
Cleansed from the vaporous passions that bedim
God's Image, sister of the Seraphim.

Fears in Solitude

Written in April 1798, during the Alarm of an Invasion

    A GREEN and silent spot, amid the hills,
    A small and silent dell ! O'er stiller place
    No singing sky-lark ever poised himself.

The hills are heathy, save that swelling slope,
Which hath a gay and gorgeous covering on,
All golden with the never-bloomless furze,
Which now blooms most profusely ; but the dell,
Bathed by the mist, is fresh and delicate
As vernal corn-field, or the unripe flax,
When, through its half-transparent stalks, at eve,
The level sunshine glimmers with green light.
Oh ! 'tis a quiet spirit-healing nook !
Which all, methinks, would love ; but chiefly he,
The humble man, who, in his youthful years,
Knew just so much of folly, as had made
His early manhood more securely wise !
Here he might lie on fern or withered heath,
While from the singing-lark (that sings unseen
The minstrelsy that solitude loves best),
And from the sun, and from the breezy air,
Sweet influences trembled o'er his frame ;
And he, with many feelings, many thoughts,
Made up a meditative joy, and found
Religious meanings in the forms of nature !
And so, his senses gradually wrapt
In a half sleep, he dreams of better worlds,
And dreaming hears thee still, O singing lark ;
That singest like an angel in the clouds !

My God ! it is a melancholy thing
For such a man, who would full fain preserve
His soul in calmness, yet perforce must feel
For all his human brethren—O my God !
It weighs upon the heart, that he must think
What uproar and what strife may now be stirring
This way or that way o'er these silent hills—
Invasion, and the thunder and the shout,
And all the crash of onset ; fear and rage,
And undetermined conflict—even now,
Even now, perchance, and in his native isle :
Carnage and groans beneath this blessed sun !

We have offended, oh ! my countrymen !
We have offended very grievously,
And been most tyrannous.   From east to west
A groan of accusation pierces Heaven !
The wretched plead against us ; multitudes
Countless and vehement, the sons of God,
Our brethren !   Like a cloud that travels on,
Steamed up from Cairo's swamps of pestilence,
Even so, my countrymen ! have we gone forth
And borne to distant tribes slavery and pangs,
And, deadlier far, our vices, whose deep taint
With slow perdition murders the whole man,
His body and his soul !   Meanwhile, at home,
All individual dignity and power
Engulfed in courts, committees, institutions,
Associations and societies,
A vain, speech-mouthing, speech-reporting guild,
One benefit-club for mutual flattery,
We have drunk up, demure as at a grace,
Pollutions from the brimming cup of wealth ;
Contemptuous of all honourable rule,
Yet bartering freedom and the poor man's life
For gold, as at a market !   The sweet words
Of Christian promise, words that even yet
Might stem destruction, were they wisely preached,
Are muttered o'er by men, whose tones proclaim
How flat and wearisome they feel their trade :
Rank scoffers some, but most too indolent
To deem them falsehoods or to know their truth.
Oh ! blasphemous ! the book of life is made
A superstitious instrument, on which
We gabble o'er the oaths we mean to break ;
For all must swear—all and in every place,
College and wharf, council and justice-court ;
All, all must swear, the briber and the bribed,
Merchant and lawyer, senator and priest,
The rich, the poor, the old man and the young ;
All, all make up one scheme of perjury,

That faith doth reel ; the very name of God
Sounds like a juggler's charm ; and, bold with joy,
Forth from his dark and lonely hiding-place,
(Portentous sight !) the owlet Atheism,
Sailing on obscene wings athwart the noon,
Drops his blue-fringed lids, and holds them close,
And hooting at the glorious Sun in Heaven,
Cries out, " Where is it ? "

                         Thankless too for peace
(Peace long preserved by fleets and perilous seas),
Secure from actual warfare, we have loved
To swell the war-whoop, passionate for war !
Alas ! for ages ignorant of all
Its ghastlier workings (famine or blue plague,
Battle, or siege, or flight through wintry-snows),
We, this whole people, have been clamorous
For war and bloodshed ; animating sports,
The which we pay for as a thing to talk of,
Spectators and not combatants ! No guess
Anticipative of a wrong unfelt,
No speculation or contingency,
However dim and vague, too vague and dim
To yield a justifying cause ; and forth
(Stuffed out with big preamble, holy names,
And adjurations of the God in Heaven,)
We send our mandates for the certain death
Of thousands and ten thousands ! Boys and girls,
And women, that would groan to see a child
Pull off an insect's leg, all read of war,
The best amusement for our morning-meal !
The poor wretch, who has learnt his only prayers
From curses, who knows scarcely words enough
To ask a blessing from his Heavenly Father,
Becomes a fluent phraseman, absolute
And technical in victories and defeats,
And all our dainty terms for fratricide ;
Terms which we trundle smoothly o'er our tongues

Like mere abstractions, empty sounds to which
We join no feeling and attach no form !
As if the soldier died without a wound ;
As if the fibres of this godlike frame
Were gored without a pang ; as if the wretch,
Who fell in battle, doing bloody deeds,
Passed off to Heaven, translated and not killed ;
As though he had no wife to pine for him,
No God to judge him ! Therefore, evil days
Are coming on us, O my countrymen !
And what if all-avenging Providence,
Strong and retributive, should make us know
The meaning of our words, force us to feel
The desolation and the agony
Of our fierce doings ?

                 Spare us yet awhile,
Father and God ! O ! spare us yet awhile !
Oh ! let not English women drag their flight
Fainting beneath the burthen of their babes,
Of the sweet infants, that but yesterday
Laughed at the breast ! Sons, brothers, husbands, all
Who ever gazed with fondness on the forms
Which grew up with you round the same fire-side,
And all who ever heard the sabbath-bells
Without the infidel's scorn, make yourselves pure !
Stand forth ! be men ! repel an impious foe,
Impious and false, a light yet cruel race,
Who laugh away all virtue, mingling mirth
With deeds of murder ; and still promising
Freedom, themselves too sensual to be free,
Poison life's amities, and cheat the heart
Of faith and quiet hope, and all that soothes
And all that lifts the spirit ! Stand we forth ;
Render them back upon the insulted ocean,
And let them toss as idly on its waves
As the vile sea-weed, which some mountain-blast
Swept from our shores ! And oh ! may we return

Not with a drunken triumph, but with fear,
Repenting of the wrongs with which we stung
So fierce a foe to frenzy !

                    I have told,
O Britons ! O my brethren ! I have told
Most bitter truth, but without bitterness.
Nor deem my zeal or factious or mis-timed ;
For never can true courage dwell with them,
Who, playing tricks with conscience, dare not look
At their own vices. We have been too long
Dupes of a deep delusion ! Some, belike,
Groaning with restless enmity, expect
All change from change of constituted power ;
As if a Government had been a robe,
On which our vice and wretchedness were tagged
Like fancy-points and fringes, with the robe
Pulled off at pleasure. Fondly these attach
A radical causation to a few
Poor drudges of chastising Providence,
Who borrow all their hues and qualities
From our own folly and rank wickedness,
Which gave them birth and nursed them. Others,
        meanwhile,
Dote with a mad idolatry ; and all
Who will not fall before their images,
And yield them worship, they are enemies
Even of their country !

                Such have I been deemed—
But, O dear Britain ! O my Mother Isle !
Needs must thou prove a name most dear and holy
To me, a son, a brother, and a friend,
A husband, and a father ! who revere
All bonds of natural love, and find them all
Within the limits of thy rocky shores.
O native Britain ! O my Mother Isle !
How shouldst thou prove aught else but dear and holy

To me, who from thy lakes and mountain-hills,
Thy clouds, thy quiet dales, thy rocks and seas,
Have drunk in all my intellectual life,
All sweet sensations, all ennobling thoughts,
All adoration of the God in nature,
All lovely and all honourable things,
Whatever makes this mortal spirit feel
The joy and greatness of its future being?
There lives nor form nor feeling in my soul
Unborrowed from my country. O divine
And beauteous island! thou hast been my sole
And most magnificent temple, in the which
I walk with awe, and sing my stately songs,
Loving the God that made me!

                                    May my fears,
My filial fears, be vain! and may the vaunts
And menace of the vengeful enemy
Pass like the gust, that roared and died away
In the distant tree: which heard, and only heard,
In this low dell, bowed not the delicate grass.

But now the gentle dew-fall sends abroad
The fruit-like perfume of the golden furze:
The light has left the summit of the hill,
Though still a sunny gleam lies beautiful,
Aslant the ivied beacon. Now farewell,
Farewell, awhile, O soft and silent spot!
On the green sheep-track, up the heathy hill,
Homeward I wind my way; and lo! recalled
From bodings that have well-nigh wearied me,
I find myself upon the brow, and pause
Startled! And after lonely sojourning
In such a quiet and surrounded nook,
This burst of prospect, here the shadowy main,
Dim tinted, there the mighty majesty
Of that huge amphitheatre of rich
And elmy fields, seems like society—

Conversing with the mind, and giving it
A livelier impulse and a dance of thought !
And now, beloved Stowey ! I behold
Thy church-tower, and, methinks, the four huge elms
Clustering, which mark the mansion of my friend ;
And close behind them, hidden from my view,
Is my own lowly cottage, where my babe
And my babe's mother dwell in peace ! With light
And quickened footsteps thitherward I tend,
Remembering thee, O green and silent dell !
And grateful, that by nature's quietness
And solitary musings, all my heart
Is softened, and made worthy to indulge
Love, and the thoughts that yearn for humankind.

Nether Stowey   April 28, 1798.

France : An Ode

I

YE Clouds ! that far above me float and pause,
    Whose pathless march no mortal may control !
    Ye Ocean-Waves ! that, wheresoe'er ye roll,
Yield homage only to eternal laws !
Ye Woods ! that listen to the night-birds singing,
    Midway the smooth and perilous slope reclined,
Save when your own imperious branches swinging,
    Have made a solemn music of the wind !
Where, like a man beloved of God,
Through glooms, which never woodman trod,
    How oft, pursuing fancies holy,
My moonlight way o'er flowering weeds I wound,
    Inspired, beyond the guess of folly,
By each rude shape and wild unconquerable sound !
O ye loud Waves ! and O ye Forests high !
    And O ye Clouds that far above me soared !
Thou rising Sun ! thou blue rejoicing Sky !

Yea, every thing that is and will be free !
Bear witness for me, wheresoe'er ye be,
With what deep worship I have still adored
    The spirit of divinest Liberty.

II

When France in wrath her giant-limbs upreared,
    And with that oath, which smote air, earth, and sea,
    Stamped her strong foot and said she would be free,
Bear witness for me, how I hoped and feared !
With what a joy my lofty gratulation
    Unawed I sang, amid a slavish band :
And when to whelm the disenchanted nation,
    Like fiends embattled by a wizard's wand,
        The Monarchs marched in evil day,
        And Britain joined the dire array ;
    Though dear her shores and circling ocean,
Though many friendships, many youthful loves,
    Had swol'n the patriot emotion,
And flung a magic light o'er all her hills and groves ;
Yet still my voice, unaltered, sang defeat
    To all that braved the tyrant-quelling lance,
And shame too long delayed and vain retreat !
For ne'er, O Liberty ! with partial aim
I dimmed thy light or damped thy holy flame ;
    But blessed the pæans of delivered France,
And hung my head and wept at Britain's name.

III

" And what," I said, " though Blasphemy's loud
        scream
    With that sweet music of deliverance strove !
    Though all the fierce and drunken passions wove
A dance more wild than e'er was maniac's dream !
    Ye storms, that round the dawning east assembled,
The Sun was rising, though ye hid his light ! "

And when, to soothe my soul, that hoped and
    trembled,
The dissonance ceased, and all seemed calm and bright;
    When France her front deep-scarred and gory
    Concealed with clustering wreaths of glory;
      When, insupportably advancing,
    Her arm made mockery of the warrior's ramp;
      While timid looks of fury glancing,
    Domestic treason, crushed beneath her fatal stamp,
Writhed like a wounded dragon in his gore;
    Then I reproached my fears that would not flee;
" And soon," I said, " shall Wisdom teach her lore
In the low huts of them that toil and groan!
And, conquering by her happiness alone,
    Shall France compel the nations to be free,
Till Love and Joy look round, and call the Earth
    their own."

IV

Forgive me, Freedom! O forgive those dreams!
    I hear thy voice, I hear thy loud lament,
    From Bleak Helvetia's icy caverns sent—
I hear thy groans upon her blood-stained streams!
Heroes, that for your peaceful country perished,
And ye that, fleeing, spot your mountain-snows
    With bleeding wounds; forgive me, that I cher-
      ished
One thought that ever blessed your cruel foes!
    To scatter rage, and traitorous guilt,
    Where Peace her jealous home had built;
      A patriot-race to disinherit
Of all that made their stormy wilds so dear;
      And with inexpiable spirit
To taint the bloodless freedom of the mountaineer—
O France, that mockest Heaven, adulterous, blind,
    And patriot only in pernicious toils,
Are these thy boasts, Champion of humankind?
    To mix with Kings in the low lust of sway,

Yell in the hunt, and share the murderous prey ;
To insult the shrine of Liberty with spoils
    From freemen torn ; to tempt and to betray ?

v

    The Sensual and the Dark rebel in vain,
    Slaves by their own compulsion ! In mad game
They burst their manacles and wear the name
    Of Freedom, graven on a heavier chain !
O Liberty ! with profitless endeavour
Have I pursued thee, many a weary hour ;
    But thou nor swell'st the victor's strain, nor ever
Didst breathe thy soul in forms of human power.
    Alike from all, howe'er they praise thee
    (Nor prayer, nor boastful name delays thee),
        Alike from Priestcraft's harpy minions,
    And factious Blasphemy's obscener slaves,
        Thou speedest on thy subtle pinions,
The guide of homeless winds, and playmate of the
        waves !
And there I felt thee !—on that sea-cliff's verge,
    Whose pines, scarce travelled by the breeze above,
Had made one murmur with the distant surge !
Yes, while I stood and gazed, my temples bare,
And shot my being through earth, sea, and air,
        Possessing all things with intensest love,
        O Liberty ! my spirit felt thee there.

February 1797.

POEMS OF LOVE BY WORDSWORTH

Poems on Lucy

STRANGE fits of passion have I known :
And I will dare to tell,
But in the Lover's ear alone,
What once to me befell.

When she I loved looked every day
Fresh as a rose in June,
I to her cottage bent my way,
Beneath an evening-moon.

Upon the moon I fixed my eye,
All over the wide lea ;
With quickening pace my horse drew nigh
Those paths so dear to me.

And now we reached the orchard-plot ;
And, as we climbed the hill,
The sinking moon to Lucy's cot
Came near, and nearer still.

In one of those sweet dreams I slept,
Kind Nature's gentlest boon !
And all the while my eyes I kept
On the descending moon.

My horse moved on ; hoof after hoof
He raised, and never stopped :
When down behind the cottage roof,
At once, the bright moon dropped.

What fond and wayward thoughts will slide
Into a Lover's head !
" O mercy ! " to myself I cried,
" If Lucy should be dead ! "

SHE dwelt among the untrodden ways
    Beside the springs of Dove,
A Maid whom there were none to praise
    And very few to love :

A violet by a mossy stone
    Half hidden from the eye !
—Fair as a star, when only one
    Is shining in the sky.

She lived unknown, and few could know
    When Lucy ceased to be ;
But she is in her grave, and, oh,
    The difference to me !

I TRAVELLED among unknown men,
    In lands beyond the sea ;
Nor, England ! did I know till then
    What love I bore to thee.

'Tis past, that melancholy dream !
    Nor will I quit thy shore
A second time ; for still I seem
    To love thee more and more.

Among thy mountains did I feel
    The joy of my desire ;
And she I cherished turned her wheel
    Beside an English fire.

Thy mornings showed, thy nights concealed
    The bowers where Lucy played ;
And thine too is the last green field
    That Lucy's eyes surveyed.

———————

THREE years she grew in sun and shower,
Then Nature said, " A lovelier flower
On earth was never sown :
This Child I to myself will take ;
She shall be mine, and I will make
A Lady of my own.

" Myself will to my darling be
Both law and impulse : and with me
The Girl, in rock and plain,
In earth and heaven, in glade and bower,
Shall feel an overseeing power
To kindle or restrain.

" She shall be sportive as the fawn
That wild with glee across the lawn,
Or up the mountain springs ;
And hers shall be the breathing balm,
And hers the silence and the calm
Of mute insensate things.

" The floating clouds their state shall lend
To her ; for her the willow bend ;
Nor shall she fail to see
Even in the motions of the Storm
Grace that shall mould the Maiden's form
By silent sympathy.

" The stars of midnight shall be dear
To her ; and she shall lean her ear
In many a secret place
Where rivulets dance their wayward round,
And beauty born of murmuring sound
Shall pass into her face.

" And vital feelings of delight
Shall rear her form to stately height,
Her virgin bosom swell ;
Such thoughts to Lucy I will give
While she and I together live
Here in this happy dell."

Thus Nature spake—The work was done—
How soon my Lucy's race was run !
She died, and left to me
This heath, this calm, and quiet scene ;
The memory of what has been,
And never more will be.

———————

A SLUMBER did my spirit seal ;
    I had no human fears :
She seemed a thing that could not feel
    The touch of earthly years.

No motion has she now, no force ;
    She neither hears nor sees ;
Rolled round in earth's diurnal course,
    With rocks, and stones, and trees.

" She was a Phantom of Delight "

SHE was a Phantom of delight
When first she gleamed upon my sight ;
A lovely Apparition, sent
To be a moment's ornament ;

Her eyes as stars of Twilight fair ;
Like Twilight's, too, her dusky hair ;
But all things else about her drawn
From May-time and the cheerful Dawn ;
A dancing Shape, an Image gay,
To haunt, to startle, and way-lay.

I saw her upon nearer view,
A Spirit, yet a Woman too !
Her household motions light and free,
And steps of virgin-liberty ;
A countenance in which did meet
Sweet records, promises as sweet ;
A Creature not too bright or good
For human nature's daily food ;
For transient sorrows, simple wiles,
Praise, blame, love, kisses, tears, and smiles.

And now I see with eye serene
The very pulse of the machine ;
A Being breathing thoughtful breath,
A Traveller between life and death ;
The reason firm, the temperate will,
Endurance, foresight, strength, and skill ;
A perfect Woman, nobly planned,
To warn, to comfort, and command ;
And yet a Spirit still, and bright
With something of angelic light.

Ruth

WHEN Ruth was left half desolate,
Her Father took another Mate ;
And Ruth, not seven years old,
A slighted child, at her own will
Went wandering over dale and hill,
In thoughtless freedom, bold

And she had made a pipe of straw,
And music from that pipe could draw
Like sounds of winds and floods ;
Had built a bower upon the green,
As if she from her birth had been
An infant of the woods.

Beneath her father's roof, alone
She seemed to live ; her thoughts her own,
Herself her own delight ;
Pleased with herself, nor sad, nor gay ;
And, passing thus the live-long day,
She grew to woman's height.

There came a Youth from Georgia's shore—
A military casque he wore,
With splendid feathers drest ;
He brought them from the Cherokees ;
The feathers nodded in the breeze,
And made a gallant crest.

From Indian blood you deem him sprung :
But no ! he spake the English tongue,
And bore a soldier's name ;
And, when America was free
From battle and from jeopardy,
He 'cross the ocean came.

With hues of genius on his cheek
In finest tones the Youth could speak :
—While he was yet a boy,
The moon, the glory of the sun,
And streams that murmur as they run,
Had been his dearest joy.

He was a lovely Youth ! I guess
The panther in the wilderness
Was not so fair as he ;

And, when he chose to sport and play,
No dolphin ever was so gay
Upon the tropic sea.

Among the Indians he had fought,
And with him many tales he brought
Of pleasure and of fear;
Such tales as told to any maid
By such a Youth, in the green shade
Were perilous to hear.

He told of girls—a happy rout!
Who quit their fold with dance and shout,
Their pleasant Indian town,
To gather strawberries all day long;
Returning with a choral song
When daylight is gone down.

He spake of plants that hourly change
Their blossoms, through a boundless range
Of intermingling hues;
With budding, fading, faded flowers
They stand the wonder of the bowers
From morn to evening dews.

He told of the magnolia, spread
High as a cloud, high over head!
The cypress and her spire;
—Of flowers that with one scarlet gleam
Cover a hundred leagues, and seem
To set the hills on fire.

The Youth of green savannahs spake,
And many an endless, endless lake,
With all its fairy crowds
Of islands, that together lie
As quietly as spots of sky
Among the evening clouds.

" How pleasant," then he said, " it were
A fisher or a hunter there,
In sunshine or in shade
To wander with an easy mind ;
And build a household fire, and find
A home in every glade !

" What days and what bright years ! Ah me !
Our life were life indeed, with thee
So passed in quiet bliss,
And all the while," said he, " to know
That we were in a world of woe,
On such an earth as this ! "

And then he sometimes interwove
Fond thoughts about a father's love ;
" For there," said he, " are spun
Around the heart such tender ties,
That our own children to our eyes
Are dearer than the sun.

" Sweet Ruth ! and could you go with me
My helpmate in the woods to be,
Our shed at night to rear ;
Or run, my own adopted bride,
A sylvan huntress at my side,
And drive the flying deer !

" Belovèd Ruth ! "—No more he said.
The wakeful Ruth at midnight shed
A solitary tear :
She thought again—and did agree
With him to sail across the sea,
And drive the flying deer.

" And now, as fitting is and right,
We in the church our faith will plight,
A husband and a wife."

Even so they did ; and I may say
That to sweet Ruth that happy day
Was more than human life.

Through dream and vision did she sink,
Delighted all the while to think
That on those lonesome floods,
And green savannahs, she should share
His board with lawful joy, and bear
His name in the wild woods.

But, as you have before been told,
This Stripling, sportive, gay, and bold,
And, with his dancing crest,
So beautiful, through savage lands
Had roamed about, with vagrant bands
Of Indians in the West.

The wind, the tempest roaring high,
The tumult of a tropic sky,
Might well be dangerous food
For him, a Youth to whom was given
So much of earth—so much of heaven,
And such impetuous blood.

Whatever in those climes he found
Irregular in sight or sound
Did to his mind impart
A kindred impulse, seemed allied
To his own powers, and justified
The workings of his heart.

Nor less, to feed voluptuous thought,
The beauteous forms of nature wrought,
Fair trees and gorgeous flowers ;
The breezes their own languor lent ;
The stars had feelings, which they sent
Into those favoured bowers.

Yet, in his worst pursuits, I ween
That sometimes there did intervene
Pure hopes of high intent :
For passions linked to forms so fair
And stately, needs must have their share
Of noble sentiment.

But ill he lived, much evil saw,
With men to whom no better law
Nor better life was known ;
Deliberately, and undeceived,
Those wild men's vices he received,
And gave them back his own.

His genius and his moral frame
Were thus impaired, and he became
The slave of low desires :
A Man who without self-control
Would seek what the degraded soul
Unworthily admires.

And yet he with no feigned delight
Had wooed the Maiden, day and night
Had loved her, night and morn :
What could he less than love a Maid
Whose heart with so much nature played ?
So kind and so forlorn !

Sometimes, most earnestly, he said,
" O Ruth ! I have been worse than dead ;
False thoughts, thoughts bold and vain,
Encompassed me on every side
When I, in confidence and pride,
Had crossed the Atlantic main.

" Before me shone a glorious world—
Fresh as a banner bright, unfurled
To music suddenly :

I looked upon those hills and plains,
And seemed as if let loose from chains,
To live at liberty.

" No more of this ; for now, by thee
Dear Ruth ! more happily set free
With nobler zeal I burn ;
My soul from darkness is released,
Like the whole sky when to the east
The morning doth return."

Full soon that better mind was gone ;
No hope, no wish remained, not one,—
They stirred him now no more ;
New objects did new pleasure give,
And once again he wished to live
As lawless as before.

Meanwhile, as thus with him it fared,
They for the voyage were prepared,
And went to the sea-shore,
But, when they thither came, the Youth
Deserted his poor Bride, and Ruth
Could never find him more.

God help thee, Ruth !—Such pains she had,
That she in half a year was mad,
And in a prison housed ;
And there, with many a doleful song
Made of wild words, her cup of wrong
She fearfully caroused.

Yet sometimes milder hours she knew,
Nor wanted sun, nor rain, nor dew,
Nor pastimes of the May ;
—They all were with her in her cell ;
And a clear brook with cheerful knell
Did o'er the pebbles play.

When Ruth three seasons thus had lain,
There came a respite to her pain ;
She from her prison fled ;
But of the Vagrant none took thought ;
And where it liked her best she sought
Her shelter and her bread.

Among the fields she breathed again :
The master-current of her brain
Ran permanent and free ;
And, coming to the Banks of Tone,
There did she rest ; and dwell alone
Under the greenwood tree.

The engines of her pain, the tools
That shaped her sorrow, rocks and pools,
And airs that gently stir
The vernal leaves—she loved them still ;
Nor ever taxed them with the ill
Which had been done to her.

A Barn her *winter* bed supplies ;
But till the warmth of summer skies
And summer days is gone,
(And all do in this tale agree)
She sleeps beneath the greenwood tree,
And other home hath none.

An innocent life, yet far astray !
And Ruth will, long before her day,
Be broken down and old :
Sore aches she needs must have ! but less
Of mind, than body's wretchedness,
From damp, and rain, and cold.

If she is prest by want of food,
She from her dwelling in the wood
Repairs to a road-side ·

And there she begs at one steep place
Where up and down with easy pace
The horsemen-travellers ride.

That oaten pipe of hers is mute,
Or thrown away ; but with a flute
Her loneliness she cheers :
This flute, made of a hemlock stalk,
At evening in his homeward walk
The Quantock woodman hears.

I, too, have passed her on the hills
Setting her little water-mills
By spouts and fountains wild—
Such small machinery as she turned
Ere she had wept, ere she had mourned,
A young and happy Child !

Farewell ! and when thy days are told,
Ill-fated Ruth, in hallowed mould
Thy corpse shall buried be,
For thee a funeral bell shall ring,
And all the congregation sing
A Christian psalm for thee.

Laodamía

" WITH sacrifice before the rising morn
Vows have I made by fruitless hope inspired ;
And from the infernal Gods, 'mid shades forlorn
Of night, my slaughtered Lord have I required :
Celestial pity I again implore ;—
Restore him to my sight—great Jove, restore ! "

So speaking, and by fervent love endowed
With faith, the Suppliant heavenward lifts her hands ;
While, like the sun emerging from a cloud,
Her countenance brightens—and her eye expands ;

Her bosom heaves and spreads, her stature grows;
And she expects the issue in repose.

O terror! what hath she perceived?—O joy!
What doth she look on?—whom doth she behold?
Her Hero slain upon the beach of Troy?
His vital presence? his corporeal mould?
It is—if sense deceive her not—'tis He!
And a God leads him, wingèd Mercury!

Mild Hermes spake—and touched her with his wand
That calms all fear; "Such grace hath crowned thy
        prayer,
Laodamía! that at Jove's command
Thy Husband walks the paths of upper air:
He comes to tarry with thee three hours' space;
Accept the gift, behold him face to face!"

Forth sprang the impassioned Queen her Lord to clasp:
Again that consummation she essayed;
But unsubstantial Form eludes her grasp
As often as that eager grasp was made.
The Phantom parts—but parts to re-unite,
And re-assume his place before her sight.

"Protesiláus, lo! thy guide is gone!
Confirm, I pray, the vision with thy voice:
This is our palace,—yonder is thy throne;
Speak, and the floor thou tread'st on will rejoice.
Not to appal me have the gods bestowed
This precious boon; and blest a sad abode."

"Great Jove, Laodamía! doth not leave
His gifts imperfect:—Spectre though I be,
I am not sent to scare thee or deceive;
But in reward of thy fidelity.
And something also did my worth obtain;
For fearless virtue bringeth boundless gain.

" Thou knowest, the Delphic oracle foretold
That the first Greek who touched the Trojan strand
Should die ; but me the threat could not withhold :
A generous cause a victim did demand ;
And forth I leapt upon the sandy plain ;
A self-devoted chief—by Hector slain."

" Supreme of Heroes—bravest, noblest, best !
Thy matchless courage I bewail no more,
Which then, when tens of thousands were deprest
By doubt, propelled thee to the fatal shore ;
Thou found'st—and I forgive thee—here thou art—
A nobler counsellor than my poor heart.

" But thou, though capable of sternest deed,
Wert kind as resolute, and good as brave ;
And he, whose power restores thee, hath decreed
Thou should'st elude the malice of the grave :
Redundant are thy locks, thy lips as fair
As when their breath enriched Thessalian air.

" No Spectre greets me,—no vain Shadow this ;
Come, blooming Hero, place thee by my side !
Give, on this well-known couch, one nuptial kiss
To me, this day, a second time thy bride ! "
Jove frowned in heaven : the conscious Parcæ threw
Upon those roseate lips a Stygian hue.

" This visage tells thee that my doom is past :
Nor should the change be mourned, even if the joys
Of sense were able to return as fast
And surely as they vanish. Earth destroys
Those raptures duly—Erebus disdains :
Calm pleasures there abide—majestic pains.

" Be taught, O faithful Consort, to control
Rebellious passion : for the Gods approve
The depth, and not the tumult, of the soul ;
A fervent, not ungovernable, love.

Thy transports moderate ; and meekly mourn
When I depart, for brief is my sojourn—"

" Ah, wherefore ?—Did not Hercules by force
Wrest from the guardian Monster of the tomb
Alcestis, a reanimated corse,
Given back to dwell on earth in vernal bloom ?
Medea's spells dispersed the weight of years,
And Æson stood a youth 'mid youthful peers.

" The Gods to us are merciful—and they
Yet further may relent : for mightier far
Than strength of nerve and sinew, or the sway
Of magic potent over sun and star,
Is love, though oft to agony distrest,
And though its favourite seat be feeble woman's
        breast.

" But if thou goest, I follow—" " Peace ! " he said,—
She looked upon him and was calmed and cheered ;
The ghastly colour from his lips had fled ;
In his deportment, shape, and mien, appeared
Elysian beauty, melancholy grace,
Brought from a pensive though a happy place.

He spake of love, such love as Spirits feel
In worlds whose course is equable and pure ;
No fears to beat away—no strife to heal—
The past unsighed for, and the future sure ;
Spake of heroic arts in graver mood
Revived, with finer harmony pursued ;

Of all that is most beauteous—imaged there
In happier beauty ; more pellucid streams,
An ampler ether, a diviner air,
And fields invested with purpureal gleams ;
Climes which the sun, who sheds the brightest day
Earth knows, is all unworthy to survey.

Yet there the Soul shall enter which hath earned
That privilege by virtue.—" Ill," said he,
" The end of man's existence I discerned,
Who from ignoble games and revelry
Could draw, when we had parted, vain delight,
While tears were thy best pastime, day and night ;

" And while my youthful peers before my eyes
(Each hero following his peculiar bent)
Prepared themselves for glorious enterprise
By martial sports,—or, seated in the tent,
Chieftains and kings in council were detained ;
What time the fleet at Aulis lay enchained.

" The wished-for wind was given :—I then revolved
The oracle, upon the silent sea ;
And, if no worthier led the way, resolved
That, of a thousand vessels, mine should be
The foremost prow in pressing to the strand,—
Mine the first blood that tinged the Trojan sand.

" Yet bitter, oft-times bitter, was the pang
When of thy loss I thought, belovèd Wife !
On thee too fondly did my memory hang,
And on the joys we shared in mortal life,—
The paths which we had trod—these fountains, flowers,
My new-planned cities, and unfinished towers.

" But should suspense permit the Foe to cry,
' Behold they tremble !—haughty their array,
Yet of their number no one dares to die ? '
In soul I swept the indignity away :
Old frailties then recurred :—but lofty thought,
In act embodied, my deliverance wrought.

" And Thou, though strong in love, art all too weak
In reason, in self-government too slow ;
I counsel thee by fortitude to seek

Our blest re-union in the shades below.
The invisible world with thee hath sympathized ;
Be thy affections raised and solemnized.

" Learn, by a mortal yearning, to ascend—
Seeking a higher object. Love was given,
Encouraged, sanctioned, chiefly for that end ;
For this the passion to excess was driven—
That self might be annulled : her bondage prove
The fetters of a dream, opposed to love."——

Aloud she shrieked ! for Hermes reappears !
Round the dear Shade she would have clung—'tis
     vain :
The hours are past—too brief had they been years ;
And him no mortal effort can detain :
Swift, toward the realms that know not earthly day,
He through the portal takes his silent way,
And on the palace-floor a lifeless corse She lay.

Thus, all in vain exhorted and reproved,
She perished ; and, as for a wilful crime,
By the just Gods whom no weak pity moved,
Was doomed to wear out her appointed time,
Apart from happy Ghosts, that gather flowers
Of blissful quiet 'mid unfading bowers.

—Yet tears to human suffering are due ;
And mortal hopes defeated and o'erthrown
Are mourned by man, and not by man alone,
As fondly he believes.—Upon the side
Of Hellespont (such faith was entertained)
A knot of spiry trees for ages grew
From out the tomb of him for whom she died ;
And ever, when such stature they had gained
That Ilium's walls were subject to their view,
The trees' tall summits withered at the sight ;
A constant interchange of growth and blight !

POEMS OF LOVE BY COLERIDGE

Love

ALL thoughts, all passions, all delights :
Whatever stirs this mortal frame,
All are but ministers of Love,
    And feed his sacred flame.

Oft in my waking dreams do I
Live o'er again that happy hour,
When midway on the mount I lay,
    Beside the ruined tower.

The moonshine, stealing o'er the scene,
Had blended with the lights of eve ;
And she was there, my hope, my joy,
    My own dear Genevieve !

She leaned against the armed man,
The statue of the armed knight ;
She stood and listened to my lay,
    Amid the lingering light.

Few sorrows hath she of her own,
My hope ! my joy ! my Genevieve !
She loves me best, whene'er I sing
    The songs that make her grieve.

I played a soft and doleful air,
I sang an old and moving story—
An old rude song, that suited well
    That ruin wild and hoary.

She listened with a flitting blush,
With downcast eyes and modest grace ;
For well she knew, I could not choose
    But gaze upon her face.

I told her of the Knight that wore
Upon his shield a burning brand ;
And that for ten long years he wooed
    The Lady of the Land.

I told her how he pined : and ah !
The deep, the low, the pleading tone
With which I sang another's love,
    Interpreted my own.

She listened with a flitting blush,
With downcast eyes, and modest grace ;
And she forgave me, that I gazed
    Too fondly on her face !

But when I told the cruel scorn
That crazed that bold and lovely Knight,
And that he crossed the mountain-woods,
    Nor rested day nor night ;

That sometimes from the savage den,
And sometimes from the darksome shade,
And sometimes starting up at once
    In green and sunny glade,—

There came and looked him in the face
An angel beautiful and bright :
And that he knew it was a Fiend,
    This miserable Knight !

And that, unknowing what he did,
He leaped amid a murderous band,
And saved from outrage worse than death
    The Lady of the Land ;—

And how she wept, and clasped his knees ;
And how she tended him in vain—
And ever strove to expiate
    The scorn that crazed his brain ;—

And that she nursed him in a cave ;
And how his madness went away,
When on the yellow forest-leaves
    A dying man he lay ;—

His dying words—but when I reached
That tenderest strain of all the ditty,
My faltering voice and pausing harp
    Disturbed her soul with pity !

All impulses of soul and sense
Had thrilled my guileless Genevieve ;
The music and the doleful tale,
    The rich and balmy eve ;

And hopes, and fears that kindle hope,
An undistinguishable throng,
And gentle wishes long subdued,
    Subdued and cherished long !

She wept with pity and delight,
She blushed with love, and virgin shame ;
And like the murmur of a dream,
    I heard her breathe my name.

Her bosom heaved—she stepped aside,
As conscious of my look she stepped—
Then suddenly, with timorous eye,
    She fled to me and wept.

She half inclosed me with her arms,
She pressed me with a meek embrace ;
And bending back her head, looked up,
    And gazed upon my face.

13

'Twas partly love, and partly fear,
And partly 'twas a bashful art,
That I might rather feel, than see,
    The swelling of her heart.

I calmed her fears, and she was calm,
And told her love with virgin pride ;
And so I won my Genevieve,
    My bright and beauteous Bride.

To Two Sisters

(MRS. MORGAN AND MISS BRENT)

A Wanderer's Farewell

To know, to esteem, to love,—and then to part—
Makes up life's tale to many a feeling heart ;
Alas for some abiding-place of love,
O'er which my spirit, like the mother dove,
Might brood with warming wings !

                           O fair ! O kind !
Sisters in blood, yet each with each intwined
More close by sisterhood of heart and mind !
Me disinherited in form and face
By nature, and mishap of outward grace ;
Who, soul and body, through one guiltless fault
Waste daily with the poison of sad thought,
Me did you soothe, when solace hoped I none !
And as on unthawed ice the winter sun,
Though stern the frost, though brief the genial day
You bless my heart with many a cheerful ray ;
For gratitude suspends the heart's despair,
Reflecting bright though cold your image there.

Nay more ! its music by some sweeter strain
Makes us live o'er our happiest hours again,

Hope re-appearing dim in memory's guise—
Even thus did you call up before mine eyes
Two dear, dear Sisters, prized all price above,
Sisters, like you, with more than sisters' love ;
So like you *they*, and so in *you* were seen
Their relative statures, tempers, looks, and mien,
That oft, dear ladies ! you have been to me
At once a vision and reality.
Sight seemed a sort of memory, and amaze
Mingled a trouble with affection's gaze.

Oft to my eager soul I whisper blame
A Stranger bid it feel the Stranger's shame—
My eager soul, impatient of the name,
No strangeness owns, no Stranger's form descries :
The chidden heart spreads trembling on the eyes.
First-seen I gazed, as I would look you thro' !
My best-beloved regained their youth in you,—
And still I ask, though now familiar grown,
Are you for *their* sakes dear, or for your own ?

O doubly dear ! may Quiet with you dwell !
In Grief I love you, yet I love you well !
Hope long is dead to me ! an orphan's tear
Love wept despairing o'er his nurse's bier.
Yet still she flutters o'er her grave's green slope :
For Love's despair is but the ghost of Hope !

Sweet Sisters ! were you placed around one hearth
With those, your other selves in shape and worth,
Far rather would I sit in solitude,
Fond recollections all my fond heart's food,
And dream of *you*, sweet Sisters ! (ah ! not mine !)
And only *dream* of you (ah ! dream and pine !)
Than boast the presence and partake the pride,
And shine in the eye, of all the world beside.

1807

Love's First Hope

O FAIR is Love's first hope to gentle mind!
As Eve's first star thro' fleecy cloudlet peeping;
And sweeter than the gentle south-west wind,
O'er willowy meads, and shadowed waters creeping,
And Ceres' golden fields;—the sultry hind
Meets it with brow uplift, and stays his reaping.

? 1824

Christabel

PREFACE [1]

THE first part of the following poem was written in the year 1797, at Stowey in the county of Somerset. The second part, after my return from Germany, in the year 1800, at Keswick, Cumberland. Since the latter date, my poetic powers have been, till very lately, in a state of suspended animation. But as, in my very first conception of the tale, I had the whole present to my mind, with the wholeness, no less than with the loveliness, of a vision; I trust that I shall yet be able to embody in verse the three parts yet to come. [2]

[1] To the edition of 1816.
[2] The poem was never finished, but the following sketch of the un-told part of the story is said to give a general idea how the poem was to have been continued and concluded:—

Over the mountains the Bard, as directed by Sir Leoline, hastes with his disciple; but in consequence of one of those inundations supposed to be common to the country, the spot only where the castle once stood is discovered, the edifice itself being washed away. He determines to return. Geraldine, being acquainted with all that is passing, like the weird sisters in *Macbeth*, vanishes. Reappearing, however, she awaits the return of the Bard, exciting in the mean-time, by her wily arts, all the anger she could rouse in the Baron's breast, as well as that jealousy of which he is described to have been susceptible.

The old Bard and the youth at length arrive, and therefore she can no longer personate the character of Geraldine, the daughter of Lord

It is probable, that if the poem had been finished at either of the former periods, or if even the first and second part had been published in the year 1800, the impression of its originality would have been much greater than I dare at present expect. But for this, I have only my own indolence to blame. The dates are mentioned for the exclusive purpose of precluding charges of plagiarism or servile imitation from myself. For there is among us a set of critics, who seem to hold that every possible thought and image is traditional; who have no notion that there are such things as fountains in the world, small as well as great; and who would therefore charitably derive every rill they behold flowing, from a perforation made in some other man's tank. I am confident, however, that as far as the present poem is concerned, the celebrated poets whose writings I might be suspected of having imitated, either in particular passages, or in the tone and the spirit of the whole, would be among the first to vindicate me from the charge, and who, on any striking coincidence, would permit me to address them in this doggerel version of two monkish Latin hexameters:

> 'Tis mine and it is likewise yours,
> But an if this will not do,
> Let it be mine, good friend! for I
> Am the poorer of the two.

Roland de Vaux, and changes her appearance to that of the accepted, though absent, lover of Christabel. Next ensues a courtship most distressing to Christabel, who feels—she knows not why—great disgust for her once favoured knight.

This coldness is very painful to the Baron, who has no more conception than herself of the supernatural transformation. She at last yields to her father's entreaties, and consents to approach the altar with the hated suitor. The real lover, returning, enters at this moment, and produces the ring which she had once given him in sign of her betrothment. Thus defeated, the supernatural being Geraldine disappears. As predicted, the castle bell tolls, the mother's voice is heard, and, to the exceeding great joy of the parties, the rightful marriage takes place, after which follows a reconciliation and explanation between father and daughter.

I have only to add, that the metre of the Christabel is not, properly speaking, irregular, though it may seem so from its being founded on a new principle : namely, that of counting in each line the accents, not the syllables. Though the latter may vary from seven to twelve, yet in each line the accents will be found to be only four. Nevertheless this occasional variation in number of syllables is not introduced wantonly, or for the mere ends of convenience, but in correspondence with some transition in the nature of the imagery or passion.

PART THE FIRST

'TIS the middle of night by the castle clock,
And the owls have awakened the crowing cock !
Tu—whit !——Tu—whoo !
And hark, again ! the crowing cock,
How drowsily it crew.

Sir Leoline, the Baron rich,
Hath a toothless mastiff, which
From her kennel beneath the rock
She maketh answer to the clock,
Four for the quarters, and twelve for the hour ;
Ever and aye, by shine and shower,
Sixteen short howls, not over loud :
Some say, she sees my lady's shroud.

Is the night chilly and dark ?
The night is chilly, but not dark.
The thin grey cloud is spread on high,
It covers but not hides the sky.
The moon is behind, and at the full ;
And yet she looks both small and dull.
The night is chill, the cloud is grey :
'Tis a month before the month of May,
And the Spring comes slowly up this way.

The lovely lady, Christabel,
Whom her father loves so well,
What makes her in the wood so late,
A furlong from the castle gate ?
She had dreams all yesternight
Of her own betrothèd knight ;
And she in the midnight wood will pray
For the weal of her lover that's far away.

She stole along, she nothing spoke,
The sighs she heaved were soft and low,
And naught was green upon the oak,
But moss and rarest misletoe :
She kneels beneath the huge oak tree,
And in silence prayeth she.

The lady sprang up suddenly,
The lovely lady, Christabel !
It moaned as near, as near can be,
But what it is, she cannot tell.—
On the other side it seems to be,
Of the huge, broad-breasted, old oak tree.

The night is chill ; the forest bare ;
Is it the wind that moaneth bleak ?
There is not wind enough in the air
To move away the ringlet curl
From the lovely lady's cheek—
There is not wind enough to twirl
The one red leaf, the last of its clan,
That dances as often as dance it can,
Hanging so light, and hanging so high,
On the topmost twig that looks up at the sky.

Hush, beating heart of Christabel !
Jesu, Maria, shield her well !
She folded her arms beneath her cloak,
And stole to the other side of the oak.
    What sees she there ?

There she sees a damsel bright,
Drest in a silken robe of white,
That shadowy in the moonlight shone :
The neck that made that white robe wan,
Her stately neck, and arms were bare :
Her blue-veined feet unsandalled were ;
And wildly glittered here and there
The gems entangled in her hair.
I guess, 'twas frightful there to see
A lady so richly clad as she—
Beautiful exceedingly !

Mary mother, save me now !
(Said Christabel), And who art thou ?

The lady strange made answer meet,
And her voice was faint and sweet :—
Have pity on my sore distress,
I scarce can speak for weariness.

Stretch forth thy hand, and have no fear,
Said Christabel, How camest thou here ?
And the lady, whose voice was faint and sweet,
Did thus pursue her answer meet :—

My sire is of a noble line,
And my name is Geraldine :
Five warriors seized me yestermorn,
Me, even me, a maid forlorn :
They choked my cries with force and fright,
And tied me on a palfrey white.
The palfrey was as fleet as wind,
And they rode furiously behind.
They spurred amain, their steeds were white ;
And once we crossed the shade of night.
As sure as Heaven shall rescue me,
I have no thought what men they be ;
Nor do I know how long it is

(For I have lain entranced I wis)
Since one, the tallest of the five,
Took me from the palfrey's back,
A weary woman, scarce alive.
Some muttered words his comrades spoke :
He placed me underneath this oak,
He swore they would return with haste ;
Whither they went I cannot tell—
I thought I heard, some minutes past,
Sounds as of a castle bell.
Stretch forth thy hand (thus ended she),
And help a wretched maid to flee.

Then Christabel stretched forth her hand
And comforted fair Geraldine :
O well bright dame may you command
The service of Sir Leoline ;
And gladly our stout chivalry
Will he send forth and friends withal
To guide and guard you safe and free
Home to your noble father's hall.
She rose : and forth with steps they passed
That strove to be, and were not, fast.
Her gracious stars the lady blest,
And thus spake on sweet Christabel :
All our household are at rest,
The hall as silent as the cell,
Sir Leoline is weak in health
And may not well awakened be,
But we will move as if in stealth :
And I beseech your courtesy
This night, to share your couch with me.

They crossed the moat, and Christabel
Took the key that fitted well ;
A little door she opened straight,
All in the middle of the gate ;

The gate that was ironed within and without,
Where an army in battle-array had marched out.
The lady sank, belike through pain,
And Christabel with might and main
Lifted her up, a weary weight,
Over the threshold of the gate :
Then the lady rose again,
And moved, as she were not in pain.

So free from danger, free from fear,
They crossed the court : right glad they were.
And Christabel devoutly cried
To the lady by her side,
Praise we the Virgin all divine
Who hath rescued thee from thy distress !
Alas, alas ! said Geraldine,
I cannot speak for weariness.
So free from danger, free from fear,
They crossed the court : right glad they were.

Outside her kennel, the mastiff old
Lay fast asleep, in moonshine cold.
The mastiff old did not awake,
Yet she an angry moan did make !
And what can ail the mastiff bitch ?
Never till now she uttered yell
Beneath the eye of Christabel.
Perhaps it is the owlet's scritch :
For what can ail the mastiff bitch ?

They passed the hall, that echoes still,
Pass as lightly as you will !
The brands were flat, the brands were dying,
Amid their own white ashes lying ;
But when the lady passed, there came
A tongue of light, a fit of flame ;
And Christabel saw the lady's eye,
And nothing else saw she thereby,

Save the boss of the shield of Sir Leoline tall,
Which hung in a murky old niche in the wall.
O softly tread, said Christabel,
My father seldom sleepeth well.

Sweet Christabel her feet doth bare,
And jealous of the listening air
They steal their way from stair to stair,
Now in glimmer, and now in gloom,
And now they pass the Baron's room,
As still as death with stifled breath !
And now have reached her chamber door ;
And now doth Geraldine press down
The rushes of the chamber floor.

The moon shines dim in the open air,
And not a moonbeam enters here.
But they without its light can see
The chamber carved so curiously,
Carved with figures strange and sweet,
All made out of the carver's brain,
For a lady's chamber meet :
The lamp with twofold silver chain
Is fastened to an angel's feet.
The silver lamp burns dead and dim ;
But Christabel the lamp will trim.
She trimmed the lamp, and made it bright,
And left it swinging to and fro,
While Geraldine, in wretched plight,
Sank down upon the floor below.

O weary lady, Geraldine,
I pray you, drink this cordial wine !
It is a wine of virtuous powers ;
My mother made it of wild flowers.

And will your mother pity me,
Who am a maiden most forlorn ?

Christabel answered—Woe is me !
She died the hour that I was born.
I have heard the grey-haired friar tell,
How on her death-bed she did say,
That she should hear the castle bell
Strike twelve upon my wedding day.
O mother dear ! that thou wert here !
I would, said Geraldine, she were !

But soon with altered voice, said she—
" Off, wandering mother !   Peak and pine !
I have power to bid thee flee."
Alas ! what ails poor Geraldine ?
Why stares she with unsettled eye ?
Can she the bodiless dead espy ?
And why with hollow voice cries she,
" Off, woman, off ! this hour is mine—
Though thou her guardian spirit be,
Off, woman, off ! 'tis given to me."

Then Christabel knelt by the lady's side,
And raised to heaven her eyes so blue—
Alas ! said she, this ghastly ride—
Dear lady ! it hath wildered you !
The lady wiped her moist cold brow,
And faintly said, " 'tis over now ! "

Again the wild-flower wine she drank :
Her fair large eyes 'gan glitter bright,
And from the floor whereon she sank,
The lofty lady stood upright ;
She was most beautiful to see,
Like a lady of a far countree.

And thus the lofty lady spake—
All they, who live in the upper sky,
Do love you, holy Christabel !
And you love them, and for their sake

And for the good which me befell,
Even I in my degree will try,
Fair maiden, to requite you well.
But now unrobe yourself ; for I
Must pray, ere yet in bed I lie.

Quoth Christabel, so let it be !
And as the lady bade, did she.
Her gentle limbs did she undress,
And lay down in her loveliness.

But through her brain of weal and woe
So many thoughts moved to and fro,
That vain it were her lids to close ;
So half-way from the bed she rose,
And on her elbow did recline
To look at the lady Geraldine.

Beneath the lamp the lady bowed,
And slowly rolled her eyes around ;
Then drawing in her breath aloud,
Like one that shuddered, she unbound
The cincture from beneath her breast :
Her silken robe, and inner vest,
Dropt to her feet, and full in view,
Behold ! her bosom and half her side—
A sight to dream of, not to tell !
O shield her ! shield sweet Christabel !

Yet Geraldine nor speaks nor stirs :
Ah ! what a stricken look was hers !
Deep from within she seems half-way
To lift some weight with sick assay,
And eyes the maid and seeks delay ;
Then suddenly, as one defied,
Collects herself in scorn and pride,
And lay down by the Maiden's side !—
And in her arms the maid she took,
        Ah, wel-a-day !

And with low voice and doleful look
      These words did say :
In the touch of this bosom there worketh a spell,
Which is lord of thy utterance, Christabel !
Thou knowest to-night, and wilt know to-morrow,
This mark of my shame, this seal of my sorrow ;
      But vainly thou warrest,
        For this is alone in
      Thy power to declare,
        That in the dim forest
      Thou heard'st a low moaning,
And found'st a bright lady, surpassingly fair :
And didst bring her home with thee in love and in
    charity,
To shield her and shelter her from the damp air.

THE CONCLUSION TO PART THE FIRST

It was a lovely sight to see
The lady Christabel, when she
Was praying at the old oak tree.
      Amid the jagged shadows
      Of mossy leafless boughs,
      Kneeling in the moonlight,
      To make her gentle vows ;
Her slender palms together prest,
Heaving sometimes on her breast ;
Her face resigned to bliss or bale—
Her face, oh call it fair not pale,
And both blue eyes more bright than clear,
Each about to have a tear.

   With open eyes (ah woe is me !)
Asleep, and dreaming fearfully,
Fearfully dreaming, yet I wis,
Dreaming that alone, which is—
O sorrow and shame !   Can this be she,
The lady who knelt at the old oak tree ?

And lo ! the worker of these harms,
That holds the maiden in her arms,
Seems to slumber still and mild,
As a mother with her child.

A star hath set, a star hath risen,
O Geraldine ! since arms of thine
Have been the lovely lady's prison.
O Geraldine ! one hour was thine—
Thou'st had thy will !   By tairn and rill,
The night-birds all that hour were still.
But now they are jubilant anew,
From cliff and tower, tu—whoo ! tu—whoo !
Tu—whoo ! tu—whoo ! from wood and fell !

And see ! the lady Christabel
Gathers herself from out her trance ;
Her limbs relax, her countenance
Grows sad and soft ; the smooth thin lids
Close o'er her eyes ; and tears she sheds—
Large tears that leave the lashes bright !
And oft the while she seems to smile
As infants at a sudden light !
Yea, she doth smile, and she doth weep,
Like a youthful hermitess,
Beauteous in a wilderness,
Who, praying always, prays in sleep.
And, if she move unquietly,
Perchance, 'tis but the blood so free,
Comes back and tingles in her feet.
No doubt, she hath a vision sweet.
What if her guardian spirit 'twere,
What if she knew her mother near ?
But this she knows, in joys and woes,
That saints will aid if men will call :
For the blue sky bends over all !

PART THE SECOND

EACH matin bell, the Baron saith,
Knells us back to a world of death.
These words Sir Leoline first said,
When he rose and found his lady dead :
These words Sir Leoline will say,
Many a morn to his dying day.

And hence the custom and law began,
That still at dawn the sacristan,
Who duly pulls the heavy bell,
Five and forty beads must tell
Between each stroke—a warning knell,
Which not a soul can choose but hear
From Bratha Head to Wyndermere.

Saith Bracy the bard, So let it knell !
And let the drowsy sacristan
Still count as slowly as he can !
There is no lack of such, I ween,
As well fill up the space between.
In Langdale Pike and Witch's Lair,
And Dungeon-ghyll so foully rent,
With ropes of rock and bells of air
Three sinful sextons' ghosts are pent,
Who all give back, one after t'other,
The death-note to their living brother ;
And oft too, by the knell offended,
Just as their one ! two ! three ! is ended,
The devil mocks the doleful tale
With a merry peal from Borrowdale.

The air is still ! through mist and cloud
That merry peal comes ringing loud ;
And Geraldine shakes off her dread,

(2,604)

14

And rises lightly from the bed ;
Puts on her silken vestments white,
And tricks her hair in lovely plight,
And nothing doubting of her spell
Awakens the lady Christabel.
" Sleep you, sweet lady Christabel ?
I trust that you have rested well."

And Christabel awoke and spied
The same who lay down by her side—
O rather say, the same whom she
Raised up beneath the old oak tree !
Nay, fairer yet ! and yet more fair !
For she belike hath drunken deep
Of all the blessedness of sleep !
And while she spake, her looks, her air
Such gentle thankfulness declare,
That (so it seemed) her girded vests
Grew tight beneath her heaving breasts.
" Sure I have sinned ! " said Christabel,
" Now Heaven be praised if all be well ! "
And in low faltering tones, yet sweet,
Did she the lofty lady greet
With such perplexity of mind
As dreams too lively leave behind.

So quickly she rose, and quickly arrayed
Her maiden limbs, and having prayed
That He, who on the cross did groan,
Might wash away her sins unknown,
She forthwith led fair Geraldine
To meet her sire, Sir Leoline.

The lovely maid and the lady tall
Are pacing both into the hall,
And pacing on through page and groom
Enter the Baron's presence room.

The Baron rose, and while he prest
His gentle daughter to his breast,
With cheerful wonder in his eyes
The lady Geraldine espies,
And gave such welcome to the same,
As might beseem so bright a dame !

But when he heard the lady's tale,
And when she told her father's name,
Why waxed Sir Leoline so pale,
Murmuring o'er the name again,
Lord Roland de Vaux of Tryermaine ?

Alas ! they had been friends in youth ;
But whispering tongues can poison truth ;
And constancy lives in realms above ;
And life is thorny ; and youth is vain ;
And to be wroth with one we love
Doth work like madness in the brain.
And thus it chanced, as I divine,
With Roland and Sir Leoline.
Each spake words of high disdain
And insult to his heart's best brother :
They parted—ne'er to meet again !
But never either found another
To free the hollow heart from paining—
They stood aloof, the scars remaining,
Like cliffs which had been rent asunder ;
A dreary sea now flows between,
But neither heat, nor frost, nor thunder,
Shall wholly do away, I ween,
The marks of that which once hath been.

Sir Leoline, a moment's space,
Stood gazing on the damsel's face ;
And the youthful Lord of Tryermaine
Came back upon his heart again.

O then the Baron forgot his age,
His noble heart swelled high with rage :
He swore by the wounds in Jesu's side,
He would proclaim it far and wide
With trump and solemn heraldry,
That they, who thus had wronged the dame,
Were base as spotted infamy !
" And if they dare deny the same,
My herald shall appoint a week,
And let the recreant traitors seek
My tourney court—that there and then
I may dislodge their reptile souls
From the bodies and forms of men ! "
He spake : his eye in lightning rolls !
For the lady was ruthlessly seized ; and he kenned
In the beautiful lady the child of his friend !

And now the tears were on his face,
And fondly in his arms he took
Fair Geraldine, who met the embrace,
Prolonging it with joyous look.
Which when she viewed, a vision fell
Upon the soul of Christabel,
The vision of fear, the touch and pain !
She shrunk and shuddered, and saw again
(Ah, woe is me !   Was it for thee,
Thou gentle maid ! such sights to see ?)
Again she saw that bosom old,
Again she felt that bosom cold,
And drew in her breath with a hissing sound :
Whereat the Knight turned wildly round,
And nothing saw, but his own sweet maid
With eyes upraised, as one that prayed.

The touch, the sight, had passed away,
And in its stead that vision blest,
Which comforted her after-rest,
While in the lady's arms she lay,

Had put a rapture in her breast,
And on her lips and o'er her eyes
Spread smiles like light !

            With new surprise,
" What ails then my beloved child ? "
The Baron said—His daughter mild
Made answer, " All will yet be well ! "
I ween, she had no power to tell
Aught else : so mighty was the spell.

Yet he, who saw this Geraldine,
Had deemed her sure a thing divine,
Such sorrow with such grace she blended,
As if she feared she had offended
Sweet Christabel, that gentle maid !
And with such lowly tones she prayed
She might be sent without delay
Home to her father's mansion.

                " Nay !
Nay, by my soul ! " said Leoline.
" Ho ! Bracy the bard, the charge be thine !
Go thou, with music sweet and loud,
And take two steeds with trappings proud,
And take the youth whom thou lov'st best
To bear thy harp, and learn thy song,
And clothe you both in solemn vest,
And over the mountains haste along,
Lest wandering folk, that are abroad,
Detain you on the valley road,
And when he has crossed the Irthing flood,
My merry bard ! he hastes, he hastes
Up Knorren Moor, through Halegarth Wood,
And reaches soon that castle good
Which stands and threatens Scotland's wastes.

" Bard Bracy ! bard Bracy ! your horses are fleet,
Ye must ride up the hall, your music so sweet,
More loud than your horses' echoing feet !

And loud and loud to Lord Roland call,
Thy daughter is safe in Langdale hall !
Thy beautiful daughter is safe and free—
Sir Leoline greets thee thus through me.
He bids thee come without delay
With all thy numerous array,
And take thy lovely daughter home ;
And he will meet thee on the way
With all his numerous array
White with their panting palfreys' foam :
And, by mine honour ! I will say,
That I repent me of the day
When I spake words of fierce disdain
To Roland de Vaux of Tryermaine !—
—For since that evil hour hath flown,
Many a summer's sun hath shone ;
Yet ne'er found I a friend again
Like Roland de Vaux of Tryermaine."

The lady fell, and clasped his knees,
Her face upraised, her eyes o'erflowing ;
And Bracy replied, with faltering voice,
His gracious hail on all bestowing :—
" Thy words, thou sire of Christabel,
Are sweeter than my harp can tell,
Yet might I gain a boon of thee,
This day my journey should not be ;
So strange a dream hath come to me ;
That I had vowed with music loud
To clear yon wood from thing unblest,
Warned by a vision in my rest !
For in my sleep I saw that dove,
That gentle bird, whom thou dost love,
And call'st by thy own daughter's name—
Sir Leoline ! I saw the same
Fluttering, and uttering fearful moan,
Among the green herbs in the forest alone.
Which when I saw and when I heard,

I wondered what might ail the bird :
For nothing near it could I see,
Save the grass and green herbs underneath the old tree.

    " And in my dream, methought, I went
To search out what might there be found :
And what the sweet bird's trouble meant,
That thus lay fluttering on the ground.
I went and peered, and could descry
No cause for her distressful cry ;
But yet for her dear lady's sake
I stooped, methought, the dove to take,
When lo ! I saw a bright green snake
Coiled around its wings and neck,
Green as the herbs on which it couched,
Close by the dove's its head it crouched ;
And with the dove it heaves and stirs,
Swelling its neck as she swelled hers !
I woke ; it was the midnight hour,
The clock was echoing in the tower ;
But though my slumber was gone by,
This dream it would not pass away—
It seems to live upon my eye !
And thence I vowed the self-same day,
With music strong and saintly song
To wander through the forest bare
Lest aught unholy loiter there."

    Thus Bracy said : the Baron, the while
Half-listening heard him with a smile ;
Then turned to Lady Geraldine
His eyes made up of wonder and love ;
And said in courtly accents fine,
" Sweet maid, Lord Roland's beauteous dove,
With arms more strong than harp or song,
Thy sire and I will crush the snake ! "
He kissed her forehead as he spake,
And Geraldine in maiden wise

Casting down her large bright eyes,
With blushing cheek and courtesy fine
She turned her from Sir Leoline ;
Softly gathering up her train,
That o'er her right arm fell again ;
And folded her arms across her chest,
And couched her head upon her breast
And looked askance at Christabel—
Jesu, Maria, shield her well !

A snake's small eye blinks dull and shy,
And the lady's eyes they shrunk in her head,
Each shrunk up to a serpent's eye,
And with somewhat of malice, and more of dread,
At Christabel she looked askance !—
One moment—and the sight was fled !
But Christabel in dizzy trance,
Stumbling on the unsteady ground—
Shuddered aloud, with a hissing sound
And Geraldine again turned round,
And like a thing, that sought relief,
Full of wonder and full of grief,
She rolled her large bright eyes divine
Wildly on Sir Leoline.

The maid, alas ! her thoughts are gone,
She nothing sees—no sight but one !
The maid, devoid of guile and sin,
I know not how, in fearful wise,
So deeply had she drunken in
That look, those shrunken serpent eyes,
That all her features were resigned
To this sole image in her mind ;
And passively did imitate
That look of dull and treacherous hate !
And thus she stood, in dizzy trance,
Still picturing that look askance
With forced unconscious sympathy

Full before her father's view—
As far as such a look could be
In eyes so innocent and blue !
And when the trance was o'er, the maid
Paused awhile, and inly prayed,
Then falling at the Baron's feet,
" By my mother's soul do I entreat
That thou this woman send away ! "
She said ; and more she could not say,
For what she knew she could not tell,
O'er-mastered by the mighty spell.

Why is thy cheek so wan and wild,
Sir Leoline ?   Thy only child
Lies at thy feet, thy joy, thy pride,
So fair, so innocent, so mild ;
The same, for whom thy lady died !
O by the pangs of her dear mother
Think thou no evil of thy child !
For her, and thee, and for no other,
She prayed the moment ere she died :
Prayed that the babe for whom she died,
Might prove her dear lord's joy and pride !
    That prayer her deadly pangs beguiled,
        Sir Leoline !
    And would'st thou wrong thy only child,
        Her child and thine ?
Within the Baron's heart and brain
If thoughts, like these, had any share,
They only swelled his rage and pain,
And did but work confusion there.
His heart was cleft with pain and rage,
His cheeks they quivered, his eyes were wild,
Dishonoured thus in his old age ;
Dishonoured by his only child,
And all his hospitality
To the wronged daughter of his friend,
By more than woman's jealousy,

POEMS OF LOVE

Brought thus to a disgraceful end—
He rolled his eye with stern regard
Upon the gentle minstrel bard,
And said in tones abrupt, austere—
" Why, Bracy ! dost thou loiter here ?
I bade thee hence ! " The bard obeyed ;
And turning from his own sweet maid,
The aged knight, Sir Leoline,
Led forth the Lady Geraldine !

THE CONCLUSION TO PART THE SECOND

A LITTLE child, a limber elf,
Singing, dancing to itself,
A fairy thing with red round cheeks
That always finds and never seeks,
Makes such a vision to the sight
As fills a father's eyes with light ;
And pleasures flow in so thick and fast
Upon his heart, that he at last
Must needs express his love's excess
With words of unmeant bitterness.
Perhaps 'tis pretty to force together
Thoughts so all unlike each other ;
To mutter and mock a broken charm,
To dally with wrong that does no harm.
Perhaps 'tis tender too and pretty
At each wild word to feel within
A sweet recoil of love and pity.
And what, if in a world of sin
(O sorrow and shame should this be true !)
Such giddiness of heart and brain
Comes seldom save from rage and pain,
So talks as it's most used to do.

POEMS OF FAITH AND EXPERIENCE
BY WORDSWORTH

" My Heart leaps up when I behold "

MY heart leaps up when I behold
    A rainbow in the sky :
So was it when my life began ;
So is it now I am a man ;
So be it when I shall grow old,
      Or let me die !
The Child is father of the Man ;
And I could wish my days to be
Bound each to each by natural piety.

Character of the Happy Warrior

WHO is the happy Warrior ?   Who is he
That every man in arms should wish to be ?
—It is the generous Spirit, who, when brought
Among the tasks of real life, hath wrought
Upon the plan that pleased his boyish thought :
Whose high endeavours are an inward light
That makes the path before him always bright :
Who, with a natural instinct to discern
What knowledge can perform, is diligent to learn ;
Abides by this resolve, and stops not there,
But makes his moral being his prime care ;
Who, doomed to go in company with Pain,

219

And Fear, and Bloodshed, miserable train !
Turns his necessity to glorious gain ;
In face of these doth exercise a power
Which is our human nature's highest dower ;
Controls them and subdues, transmutes, bereaves
Of their bad influence, and their good receives :
By objects, which might force the soul to abate
Her feeling, rendered more compassionate ;
Is placable—because occasions rise
So often that demand such sacrifice ;
More skilful in self-knowledge, even more pure,
As tempted more ; more able to endure,
As more exposed to suffering and distress ;
Thence, also, more alive to tenderness.
—'Tis he whose law is reason ; who depends
Upon that law as on the best of friends ;
Whence, in a state where men are tempted still
To evil for a guard against worse ill,
And what in quality or act is best
Doth seldom on a right foundation rest,
He labours good on good to fix, and owes
To virtue every triumph that he knows :
—Who, if he rise to station of command,
Rises by open means ; and there will stand
On honourable terms, or else retire,
And in himself possess his own desire :
Who comprehends his trust, and to the same
Keeps faithful with a singleness of aim ;
And therefore does not stoop, nor lie in wait
For wealth, or honours, or for worldly state ;
Whom they must follow ; on whose head must fall,
Like showers of manna, if they come at all :
Whose powers shed round him in the common strife,
Or mild concerns of ordinary life,
A constant influence, a peculiar grace ;
But who, if he be called upon to face
Some awful moment to which Heaven has joined
Great issues, good or bad for human kind,

Is happy as a Lover ; and attired
With sudden brightness, like a Man inspired ;
And, through the heat of conflict, keeps the law
In calmness made, and sees what he foresaw ;
Or if an unexpected call succeed,
Come when it will, is equal to the need :
—He who, though thus endued as with a sense
And faculty for storm and turbulence,
Is yet a Soul whose master-bias leans
To homefelt pleasures and to gentle scenes ;
Sweet images ! which, wheresoe'er he be,
Are at his heart ; and such fidelity
It is his darling passion to approve ;
More brave for this, that he hath much to love :—
'Tis, finally, the Man, who, lifted high,
Conspicuous object in a Nation's eye,
Or left unthought-of in obscurity,—
Who, with a toward or untoward lot,
Prosperous or adverse, to his wish or not—
Plays, in the many games of life, that one
Where what he most doth value must be won :
Whom neither shape of danger can dismay,
Nor thought of tender happiness betray ;
Who, not content that former worth stand fast,
Looks forward, persevering to the last,
From well to better, daily self-surpast :
Who, whether praise of him must walk the earth
For ever, and to noble deeds give birth,
Or he must fall, to sleep without his fame,
And leave a dead unprofitable name—
Finds comfort in himself and in his cause ;
And, while the mortal mist is gathering, draws
His breath in confidence of Heaven's applause :
This is the happy Warrior ; this is He
That every Man in arms should wish to be.

Ode to Duty

[" Jam non consilio bonus, sed more eò perductus, ut non tantum
rectè facere possim, sed nisi rectè facere non possim."]

STERN Daughter of the Voice of God !
O Duty ! if that name thou love
Who art a light to guide, a rod
To check the erring, and reprove ;
Thou, who art victory and law
When empty terrors overawe ;
From vain temptations dost set free ;
And calm'st the weary strife of frail humanity !
There are who ask not if thine eye
Be on them ; who, in love and truth,
Where no misgiving is, rely
Upon the genial sense of youth :
Glad Hearts ! without reproach or blot
Who do thy work, and know it not :
Oh ! if through confidence misplaced
They fail, thy saving arms, dread Power ! around
    them cast.

Serene will be our days and bright,
And happy will our nature be,
When love is an unerring light,
And joy its own security.
And they a blissful course may hold
Even now, who, not unwisely bold,
Live in the spirit of this creed ;
Yet seek thy firm support, according to their need.

I, loving freedom, and untried ;
No sport of every random gust,
Yet being to myself a guide,
Too blindly have reposed my trust :

And oft, when in my heart was heard
Thy timely mandate, I deferred
The task, in smoother walks to stray ;
But thee I now would serve more strictly, if I may.

Through no disturbance of my soul,
Or strong compunction in me wrought,
I supplicate for thy control ;
But in the quietness of thought :
Me this unchartered freedom tires ;
I feel the weight of chance-desires :
My hopes no more must change their name,
I long for a repose that ever is the same.

Stern Lawgiver ! yet thou dost wear
The Godhead's most benignant grace ;
Nor know we anything so fair
As is the smile upon thy face :
Flowers laugh before thee on their beds
And fragrance in thy footing treads ;
Thou dost preserve the stars from wrong ;
And the most ancient heavens, through Thee, are
    fresh and strong.

To humbler functions, awful Power !
I call thee : I myself commend
Unto thy guidance from this hour ;
Oh, let my weakness have an end !
Give unto me, made lowly wise,
The spirit of self-sacrifice ;
The confidence of reason give ;
And in the light of truth thy Bondman let me live !

Ode

Intimations of Immortality from Recollections of Early Childhood

" The Child is Father of the Man ;
And I could wish my days to be
Bound each to each by natural piety."

THERE was a time when meadow, grove, and stream,
The earth, and every common sight,
        To me did seem
        Apparelled in celestial light,
The glory and the freshness of a dream.
It is not now as it hath been of yore ;—
        Turn wheresoe'er I may,
        By night or day,
The things which I have seen I now can see no more.
        The Rainbow comes and goes,
        And lovely is the Rose,
        The Moon doth with delight
    Look round her when the heavens are bare,
        Waters on a starry night
        Are beautiful and fair ;
    The sunshine is a glorious birth ;
    But yet I know, where'er I go,
That there hath past away a glory from the earth.

Now, while the birds thus sing a joyous song,
        And while the young lambs bound
        As to the tabor's sound,
To me alone there came a thought of grief :
A timely utterance gave that thought relief,
        And I again am strong :
The cataracts blow their trumpets from the steep ;
No more shall grief of mine the season wrong ;
I hear the Echoes through the mountains throng,

The Winds come to me from the fields of sleep,
  And all the earth is gay ;
   Land and sea
  Give themselves up to jollity,
   And with the heart of May
  Doth every Beast keep holiday ;—
   Thou Child of Joy,
Shout round me, let me hear thy shouts, thou happy
   Shepherd-boy !

Ye blessèd Creatures, I have heard the call
  Ye to each other make ; I see
The heavens laugh with you in your jubilee ;
  My heart is at your festival,
  My head hath its coronal,
The fulness of your bliss, I feel—I feel it all.
   Oh evil day ! if I were sullen
   While Earth herself is adorning,
    This sweet May-morning,
   And the Children are culling
    On every side,
  In a thousand valleys far and wide,
  Fresh flowers ; while the sun shines warm,
And the Babe leaps up on his Mother's arm :—
  I hear, I hear, with joy I hear !
  —But there's a Tree, of many, one,
A single Field which I have looked upon,
Both of them speak of something that is gone :
  The Pansy at my feet
  Doth the same tale repeat :
Whither is fled the visionary gleam ?
Where is it now, the glory and the dream ?

Our birth is but a sleep and a forgetting :
The Soul that rises with us, our life's Star,
  Hath had elsewhere its setting,
   And cometh from afar :
(2,604)

Not in entire forgetfulness,
And not in utter nakedness,
But trailing clouds of glory do we come
From God, who is our home :
Heaven lies about us in our infancy !
Shades of the prison-house begin to close
Upon the growing Boy,
But He beholds the light, and whence it flows,
He sees it in his joy ;
The Youth, who daily farther from the east
Must travel, still is Nature's Priest,
And by the vision splendid
Is on his way attended ;
At length the Man perceives it die away,
And fade into the light of common day.

Earth fills her lap with pleasures of her own ;
Yearnings she hath in her own natural kind,
And, even with something of a Mother's mind,
And no unworthy aim,
The homely Nurse doth all she can
To make her Foster-child, her Inmate Man,
Forget the glories he hath known,
And that imperial palace whence he came.

Behold the Child among his new-born blisses,
A six years' Darling of a pigmy size !
See, where 'mid work of his own hand he lies,
Fretted by sallies of his mother's kisses,
With light upon him from his father's eyes !
See, at his feet, some little plan or chart,
Some fragment from his dream of human life,
Shaped by himself with newly-learned art ;
A wedding or a festival,
A mourning or a funeral ;
And this hath now his heart,
And unto this he frames his song :
Then will he fit his tongue

To dialogues of business, love, or strife ;
　　But it will not be long
　　Ere this be thrown aside,
　　And with new joy and pride
The little Actor cons another part ;
Filling from time to time his " humorous stage "
With all the Persons, down to palsied Age,
That Life brings with her in her equipage ;
　　As if his whole vocation
　　Were endless imitation.

Thou, whose exterior semblance doth belie
　　Thy Soul's immensity ;
Thou best Philosopher, who yet dost keep
Thy heritage, thou Eye among the blind,
That, deaf and silent, read'st the eternal deep,
Haunted for ever by the eternal mind,—
　　Mighty Prophet ! Seer blest !
　　On whom those truths do rest,
Which we are toiling all our lives to find,
In darkness lost, the darkness of the grave ;
Thou, over whom thy Immortality
Broods like the Day, a Master o'er a Slave,
A Presence which is not to be put by ;
Thou little Child, yet glorious in the might
Of heaven-born freedom on thy being's height,
Why with such earnest pains dost thou provoke
The years to bring the inevitable yoke,
Thus blindly with thy blessedness at strife ?
Full soon thy Soul shall have her earthly freight,
And custom lie upon thee with a weight,
Heavy as frost, and deep almost as life !

　　O joy ! that in our embers
　　Is something that doth live,
　　That nature yet remembers
　　What was so fugitive !

The thought of our past years in me doth breed
Perpetual benediction : not indeed
For that which is most worthy to be blest—
Delight and liberty, the simple creed
Of Childhood, whether busy or at rest,
With new-fledged hope still fluttering in his breast :—
  Not for these I raise
  The song of thanks and praise ;
 But for those obstinate questionings
 Of sense and outward things,
 Fallings from us, vanishings ;
 Blank misgivings of a Creature
Moving about in worlds not realized,
High instincts before which our mortal Nature
Did tremble like a guilty Thing surprised :
  But for those first affections,
  Those shadowy recollections,
 Which, be they what they may,
Are yet the fountain light of all our day,
Are yet a master light of all our seeing ;
 Uphold us, cherish, and have power to make
Our noisy years seem moments in the being
Of the eternal Silence : truths that wake,
  To perish never ;
Which neither listlessness, nor mad endeavour,
  Nor Man nor Boy,
Nor all that is at enmity with joy,
Can utterly abolish or destroy !
  Hence in a season of calm weather
  Though inland far we be,
Our Souls have sight of that immortal sea
  Which brought us hither,
  Can in a moment travel thither,
And see the Children sport upon the shore,
And hear the mighty waters rolling evermore.

Then sing, ye Birds, sing, sing a joyous song !
  And let the young Lambs bound

As to the tabor's sound !
We in thought will join your throng,
Ye that pipe and ye that play,
Ye that through your hearts to-day
Feel the gladness of the May !
What though the radiance which was once so bright
Be now for ever taken from my sight,
Though nothing can bring back the hour
Of splendour in the grass, of glory in the flower ;
We will grieve not, rather find
Strength in what remains behind ;
In the primal sympathy
Which having been must ever be ;
In the soothing thoughts that spring
Out of human suffering ;
In the faith that looks through death,
In years that bring the philosophic mind.

And O, ye Fountains, Meadows, Hills, and Groves,
Forebode not any severing of our loves !
Yet in my heart of hearts I feel your might ;
I only have relinquished one delight
To live beneath your more habitual sway.
I love the Brooks which down their channels fret,
Even more than when I tripped lightly as they ;
The innocent brightness of a new-born Day
Is lovely yet ;
The Clouds that gather round the setting sun
Do take a sober colouring from an eye
That hath kept watch o'er man's mortality ;
Another race hath been, and other palms are won.
Thanks to the human heart by which we live,
Thanks to its tenderness, its joys, and fears,
To me the meanest flower that blows can give
Thoughts that do often lie too deep for tears.

POEMS OF FAITH AND EXPERIENCE
BY COLERIDGE

Dejection : An Ode

> Late, late yestreen I saw the new Moon,
> With the old Moon in her arms;
> And I fear, I fear, my Master dear!
> We shall have a deadly storm.
> BALLAD OF SIR PATRICK SPENCE.

I

WELL!   If the Bard was weather-wise who made
  The grand old ballad of Sir Patrick Spence,
    This night, so tranquil now, will not go hence
Unroused by winds, that ply a busier trade
Than those which mould yon cloud in lazy flakes,
Or the dull sobbing draft, that moans and rakes
    Upon the strings of this Eolian lute,
    Which better far were mute.
For lo! the new Moon winter-bright!
And overspread with phantom light
(With swimming phantom light o'erspread
    But rimmed and circled by a silver thread),
I see the old Moon in her lap, foretelling
    The coming on of rain and squally blast.
And oh! that even now the gust were swelling,
  And the slant night-shower driving loud and fast!
Those sounds which oft have raised me, whilst they
      awed,
    And sent my soul abroad,

230

Might now perhaps their wonted impulse give,
Might startle this dull pain, and make it move and
       live !

II

A grief without a pang, void, dark, and drear,
   A stifled, drowsy, unimpassioned grief,
   Which finds no natural outlet, no relief,
      In word, or sigh, or tear—
O Lady ! in this wan and heartless mood,
To other thoughts by yonder throstle woo'd,
   All this long eve, so balmy and serene,
Have I been gazing on the western sky,
   And its peculiar tint of yellow green :
And still I gaze—and with how blank an eye !
And those thin clouds above, in flakes and bars,
That give away their motion to the stars ;
Those stars, that glide behind them or between,
Now sparkling, now bedimmed, but always seen :
Yon crescent Moon as fixed as if it grew
In its own cloudless, starless lake of blue ;
I see them all so excellently fair,
I see, not feel, how beautiful they are !

III

     My genial spirits fail ;
     And what can these avail
To lift the smothering weight from off my breast ?
     It were a vain endeavour,
     Though I should gaze for ever
On that green light that lingers in the west :
I may not hope from outward forms to win
The passion and the life, whose fountains are within.

IV

O Lady ! we receive but what we give,
And in our life alone does nature live :

Ours is her wedding garment, ours her shroud !
  And would we aught behold, of higher worth,
Than that inanimate cold world allowed
To the poor loveless ever-anxious crowd,
  Ah ! from the soul itself must issue forth,
A light, a glory, a fair luminous cloud
        Enveloping the Earth—
And from the soul itself must there be sent
  A sweet and potent voice, of its own birth,
Of all sweet sounds the life and element !

V

O pure of heart ! thou need'st not ask of me
What this strong music in the soul may be !
What, and wherein it doth exist,
This light, this glory, this fair luminous mist,
This beautiful and beauty-making power.
  Joy, virtuous Lady ! Joy that ne'er was given,
Save to the pure, and in their purest hour,
Life, and Life's effluence, cloud at once and shower,
Joy, Lady ! is the spirit and the power,
Which wedding Nature to us gives in dower,
  A new Earth and new Heaven,
Undreamt of by the sensual and the proud—
Joy is the sweet voice, Joy the luminous cloud—
      We in ourselves rejoice !
And thence flows all that charms or ear or sight,
  All melodies the echoes of that voice,
All colours a suffusion from that light.

VI

There was a time when, though my path was rough,
  This joy within me dallied with distress,
And all misfortunes were but as the stuff
    Whence Fancy made me dreams of happiness :

For hope grew round me, like the twining vine,
And fruits, and foliage, not my own, seemed mine.
But now afflictions bow me down to earth :
Nor care I that they rob me of my mirth,
    But oh ! each visitation
Suspends what nature gave me at my birth,
   My shaping spirit of Imagination.
For not to think of what I needs must feel,
   But to be still and patient, all I can ;
And haply by abstruse research to steal
   From my own nature all the natural man—
   This was my sole resource, my only plan :
Till that which suits a part infects the whole,
And now is almost grown the habit of my soul.

VII

Hence, viper thoughts, that coil around my mind,
      Reality's dark dream !
I turn from you, and listen to the wind,
   Which long has raved unnoticed.   What a scream
Of agony by torture lengthened out
That lute sent forth !   Thou Wind, that ravest with-
      out,
   Bare craig, or mountain tairn,* or blasted tree,
Or pine-grove whither woodman never clomb,
Or lonely house, long held the witches' home,
   Methinks were fitter instruments for thee,
Mad Lutanist ! who in this month of showers,
Of dark brown gardens, and of peeping flowers,
Mak'st Devils' yule, with worse than wintry song,
The blossoms, buds, and timorous leaves among.
   Thou Actor, perfect in all tragic sounds !

---

* Tairn is a small lake, generally, if not always, applied to the
lakes up in the mountains, and which are the feeders of those in the
valleys.   This address to the Storm-wind will not appear extrava-
gant to those who have heard it at night, and in a mountainous
country.

Thou mighty Poet, e'en to frenzy bold !
    What tell'st thou now about ?
      'Tis of the rushing of a host in rout,
  With groans of trampled men, with smarting
        wounds—
At once they groan with pain, and shudder with the
      cold !
But hush ! there is a pause of deepest silence !
    And all that noise, as of a rushing crowd,
With groans, and tremulous shudderings—all is over—
    It tells another tale, with sounds less deep and loud !
      A tale of less affright,
      And tempered with delight,
As Otway's self had framed the tender lay,
      'Tis of a little child
      Upon a lonesome wild,
Not far from home, but she hath lost her way :
And now moans low in bitter grief and fear,
And now screams loud, and hopes to make her mother
      hear.

VIII

'Tis midnight, but small thoughts have I of sleep :
Full seldom may my friend such vigils keep !
Visit her, gentle Sleep ! with wings of healing,
    And may this storm be but a mountain-birth,
May all the stars hang bright above her dwelling,
    Silent as though they watched the sleeping Earth !
      With light heart may she rise,
      Gay fancy, cheerful eyes,
    Joy lift her spirit, joy attune her voice ;
To her may all things live, from pole to pole,
Their life the eddying of her living soul !
    O simple spirit, guided from above,
Dear Lady ! friend devoutest of my choice,
Thus mayest thou ever, evermore rejoice.

Youth and Age

VERSE, a breeze 'mid blossoms straying,
Where Hope clung feeding, like a bee—
Both were mine ! Life went a-maying
      With Nature, Hope, and Poesy,
            When I was young !
When I was young ?—Ah, woeful When !
Ah for the change 'twixt Now and Then !
This breathing house, not built with hands,
This body that does me grievous wrong,
O'er aery cliffs and glittering sands,
How lightly then it flashed along :—
Like those trim skiffs, unknown of yore,
On winding lakes and rivers wide,
That ask no aid of sail or oar,
That fear no spite of wind or tide !
Nought cared this body for wind or weather
When Youth and I lived in't together.

Flowers are lovely ; Love is flower-like ;
Friendship is a sheltering tree ;
O ! the joys, that came down shower-like,
Of Friendship, Love, and Liberty,
            Ere I was old !

Ere I was old ? Ah woeful Ere !
Which tells me Youth's no longer here !
O Youth ! for years so many and sweet,
'Tis known that Thou and I were one,
I'll think it but a fond conceit—
It cannot be that Thou art gone !
Thy vesper-bell hath not yet tolled :—
And thou wert aye a masker bold !
What strange disguise hast now put on,
To *make believe*, that Thou art gone ?

I see these locks, in silvery slips,
This drooping gait, this altered size ;
But springtide blossoms on thy lips,
And tears take sunshine from thine eyes !
Life is but thought : so think I will
That Youth and I are house-mates still.

Human Life

On the Denial of Immortality

If dead, we cease to be ; if total gloom
    Swallow up life's brief flash for aye, we fare
As summer-gusts, of sudden birth and doom,
    Whose sound and motion not alone declare,
But are their whole of being ! If the breath
    Be life itself, and not its task and tent,
If even a soul like Milton's can know death ;
    O Man ! thou vessel purposeless, unmeant,
Yet drone-hive strange of phantom purposes !
    Surplus of nature's dread activity,
Which, as she gazed on some nigh-finished vase
Retreating slow, with meditative pause,
    She formed with restless hands unconsciously !
Blank accident ! nothing's anomaly !
    If rootless thus, thus substanceless thy state,
Go, weigh thy dreams, and be thy hopes, thy fears,
The counter-weights !—Thy laughter and thy tears
    Mean but themselves, each fittest to create,
And to repay the other ! Why rejoices
    Thy heart with hollow joy for hollow good ?
Why cowl thy face beneath the mourner's hood,
    Why waste thy sighs, and thy lamenting voices,
    Image of image, ghost of ghostly elf,
That such a thing as thou feel'st warm or cold ?

Yet what and whence thy gain, if thou withhold
   These costless shadows of thy shadowy self ?
Be sad ! be glad ! be neither ! seek, or shun !
Thou hast no reason why !   Thou canst have none ;
Thy being's being is contradiction.

AN EPITAPH BY WORDSWORTH

From " A Poet's Epitaph "

BUT who is He, with modest looks,
And clad in homely russet brown?
He murmurs near the running brooks
A music sweeter than their own.

He is retired as noontide dew,
Or fountain in a noon-day grove;
And you must love him, ere to you
He will seem worthy of your love.

The outward shows of sky and earth,
Of hill and valley, he has viewed;
And impulses of deeper birth
Have come to him in solitude.

In common things that round us lie
Some random truths he can impart,—
The harvest of a quiet eye
That broods and sleeps on his own heart.

But he is weak; both Man and Boy,
Hath been an idler in the land;
Contented if he might enjoy
The things which others understand.

—Come hither in thy hour of strength;
Come, weak as is a breaking wave!
Here stretch thy body at full length;
Or build thy house upon this grave.

AN EPITAPH BY COLERIDGE

STOP, Christian passer-by! Stop, child of God,
And read with gentle breast.   Beneath this sod
A poet lies, or that which once seemed he.—
O, lift one thought in prayer for S.T.C. ;
That he who many a year with toil of breath
Found death in life, may here find life in death !
Mercy for praise—to be forgiven for fame
He asked, and hoped, through Christ.
          Do thou the same !

November 9, 1833.

THE END

**PRINTED IN GREAT BRITAIN AT
THE PRESS OF THE PUBLISHERS**